Walter Reed

Walter Reed

A BIOGRAPHY

by William B. Bean, M.D.

UNIVERSITY PRESS OF VIRGINIA
Charlottesville

Endpapers: Second Division Hospital, Camp Columbia, Havana, Cuba,
April 1899. Some of Walter Reed's tests and writing were done in the building
just to the right of center, which served as office and laboratory. (Courtesy,
U.S. Army Medical Museum, neg. no. 67355.)
Title page: The Walter Reed medal, given posthumously to Reed's widow and
also awarded to those Americans who got yellow fever or participated
in the fomites experiments during the studies. (Courtesy, National Library of
Medicine, Bethesda, Md.)

THE UNIVERSITY PRESS OF VIRGINIA
Copyright © 1982 by the Rector and Visitors
of the University of Virginia

First published 1982

Library of Congress Cataloging in Publication Data
Bean, William Bennett.
 Walter Reed.
 Includes index.
 1. Reed, Walter, 1851–1902. 2. Pathologists—
United States—Biography. 3. United States.
Army—Surgeons—Biography. I. Title.
RB17.R43B4   610'.92'4 [B]   81–16123
ISBN 0–8139–0913–9   AACR2

Printed in the United States of America

TO
all those
conscientious and courageous
investigators and volunteers who
have made possible and enhanced the
health of today's forgetful people

Contents

Preface

Fifty years spent in medicine, dealing with the dying and with those grappling perhaps for the first time with the possibility of death, have led me to speculate about what happens to a person when his physical body dies. I cannot claim to have seen a ghost; but as a physician I am profoundly aware of men now gone whose hands guide mine, and whose intuitions, often greeted initially with scorn and opposition, laid the base for all I know about my profession. Anyone trying to unlock the secrets of nature is, of course, in debt to his predecessors. But medical advances have come so rapidly since the last decade of the last century that our predecessors seem to be vanishing only now.

We give due recognition to many of them through the eponym, speaking of So-and-So's sign, syndrome, tumor, or device. Our memory is shorter, however, when it comes to those whose work overcame some pestilence with which, thanks to them, we are no longer familiar even through hearsay. Fearful now about the possibilities of nuclear disaster and pollution, we know nothing of the terror of epidemic disease that until recently constituted the

PREFACE

dark side of what we now regard complacently, and even with envy, as a time of confidence and homely comfort.

Perhaps I was drawn to one such conqueror of pestilence —Walter Reed—because I grew up in the small "academical village" in which he had his medical training shortly after the Civil War. Virginians have long memories, and in the nostalgic loveliness of Mr. Jefferson's completed dream at the University of Virginia, it is possible even now to imagine an antiquated coattail whisking around a corner. It is natural for anyone raised in this place to sense the humanity of those whose lives unfolded here, and to long to know them truly.

I have spent much time over a number of years trying to discover the Walter Reed who helped to control yellow fever. I traveled where he had traveled and lived, interviewed members of his family still living and people who remembered family accounts of him, and pored over letters that often artlessly revealed his pain, disappointment, and persistent hope. They disclosed at the same time glimpses of American experience before the shattering changes that were initiated by two world wars and were continued by scientific and social revolution. Fortunately, I am myself old enough to avoid falling into the error of regarding what is past as simply quaint. I am able to appreciate the social, economic, and physical circumstances, so different from those of the present, that governed conduct in Reed's lifetime. Patronizing hindsight is a great distorter of reality; we too would have bowed to the expectations of the time, although his life may now appear to us to have been meager and inhibited in spite of the opening of new lands during that period and the prevailing belief in progress. But few among us would have persevered with so little encouragement, so little pay or honor, and under conditions of such physical discomfort as did Walter Reed, who was only briefly, and at the end, a hero.

Words of Gratitude

For a novice to travel the rocky road of biography, boldness and courage are not enough. He needs help in large quantities. This I have received. Properly to thank everyone would take an impossible amount of space. During the nearly fifteen years of my searches I have received formal and informal help from an ever-lengthening list of people. One begins with parents, siblings, friends, and teachers during the period in which growth advances toward maturity. Education continues. Several groups of people were extremely helpful. These include surviving members of the family of Walter Reed and his wife, Emilie Lawrence; libraries and librarians; universities; Army medical officers; editorial assistants; secretaries; historians; state historical societies; friends; and colleagues.

Dr. Philip Hench's interest in yellow fever and in Walter Reed matured when Walter Reed's widow and two children were very much alive for interviews and discussions. Ultimately, many Reed letters came to the University of Virginia. In the 1940s Hench interviewed surviving volunteers or the families of volunteers for the yellow fever studies. Walter Reed's son, Lawrence, had a daughter, Daisy, who married Gen. Charles Royce—all now dead. From them I got Daisy's father's schoolboy letters

WORDS OF GRATITUDE

home, a copy of Reed's account book, and pictures of Lawrence as a five-year-old.

I met many of Walter Reed's nieces and nephews, the children and grandchildren of Laura Reed Blincoe, James Reed, Tom Reed, and Christopher Reed. One day I was able to see four of James Reed's children: Walter Reed, Alice Reed, Elizabeth Reed, and Mrs. Battin, in Amherst. From them I got invaluable help in identifying certain mysterious people and places in Walter Reed's early letters to Emilie Lawrence, and later I obtained a letter from a great-nephew, Mr. Bowman. Of particular help was Sallie Robberts, who vividly recalled the injury of her father, Tom Reed, and her visit to Walter Reed's home at Fort Sidney. Christopher Reed's descendents were able to supply important information about him.

At my urging and with his wife's detective work, the late William Blincoe, a great-nephew of Walter Reed, resurrected long-forgotten letters Walter Reed had written to his sister, Laura, William Blincoe's grandmother. William Blincoe with another great-nephew, Edward Graves, an old friend, led me on merry hunts through northeastern North Carolina looking up Reed and Lawrence deeds and ancestry.

Gorgas's daughter, Eileen Gorgas Wrightson, put me on the trail of the Gorgas-Reed letters, which she had given to her cousin, Colonel Lyster. They had wound up in the library of the Medical Society of Denver, where the librarian and Brad Rodgers finally ran them to ground for me.

Dr. Caroline Bedell Thomas provided much information about Keewaydin and Blue Ridge Summit.

I have had invaluable help from three universities. The University of Virginia offered the resources of the Hench Collection and the support of the Macy Foundation, Dr. Thomas Hunter, Dr. William Mott, Dr. Byrd Leavell, Deans Drucker and Knorr, and Presidents Shannon and Hereford, which permitted me to spend two half years working on Reed material. I have had the delightful experience of having my office next door to that prince of Jefferson biographers, Dumas Malone, and had ample opportunity to discuss various matters with him, Todd L. Savitt, and others.

The Commonwealth Foundation was of great assistance in providing for some editorial and secretarial work. During eight years the University of Iowa provided unexcelled secretarial assistance from Miss Phyllis Shay, and the University Library

Words of Gratitude

had complete files of the *Army-Navy Journal*, the Annual Reports of the Surgeon General to the Secretary of War, and many other sources of great assistance.

Presidents Truman Blocker and William Levin at the University of Texas Medical Branch in Galveston, with its superb Moody Medical Library, were steady in help and support. Mrs. Beverly DeVries was a splendid secretary. The professional editorial skills of Mrs. Virginia Kennan, supported by the University of Virginia, helped me with the procrustean requirements of bringing the biography down to manageable size. For six years Mrs. Dodie Meeks, editorial girl Friday, blended her versions with mine. The enthusiasm, imagination, and patience of all these essential helpers have gone far beyond the call of duty.

Libraries, a part of my lifelong habitat, have been of invaluable aid. John Wyllie of the Alderman Library at the University of Virginia, an old classmate of mine, made working on the Hench papers—under the care of Edmund Berkeley and Miss Anne Freudenberg, as well as Miss Purvis—a great pleasure. The National Library of Medicine, with particular help from Dr. Martin Cummings, Dr. John Blake, Dr. Peter Olch, and Dr. Wyndham Miles were helpful with suggestions at all turns. Dr. Chauncey Leake, helpful in many ways, purloined for me from his brother his presentation copy of his edition of Ashbel Smith's story of yellow fever in Galveston. The National Archives were unfailingly helpful, letting me discover one treasure trove after another, especially in the Military Records section. The same was true of the Armed Forces Institute of Pathology, lineal descendent of the old Army Medical Museum. The staff of the Walter Reed Hospital has helped in many ways. The libraries of several state historical societies, particularly Virginia, Iowa, Nebraska, ard Arizona, have been most helpful. University libraries and librarians at Vanderbilt and Alabama have been extremely helpful.

Gertrude Annan, librarian of the New York Academy of Medicine, with help from Laura Wood, located one of Lazear's two missing notebooks. The other has vanished.

Quincy Mumford at the Library of Congress had the building opened for me on a holiday, and in a brief time, I found two letters of congratulations Reed had written Leonard Wood.

I had valuable correspondence with General Truby's daughter, Elizabeth; the McPherson family; the Walter Reed Weaver family; Don MacIntire, who had many Walter Reed books given by Reed's daughter, Blossom; and Lawrence Kohn, who told me about Reed's appearing in McCullough's book, *The Bridge.*

Mrs. Crosby Roper (when she was Laura Wood) wrote a splendid biography of Reed—ostensibly for juveniles, but the best biography we have. She has turned over to me boxes of her research material, now at the University of Virginia.

The Army taught me much during my four years as a medical officer in the Army Medical Laboratory at Fort Knox and in various parts of the Pacific and the United States. A number of people have been helpful, particularly after their retirement from active duty. Dr. Stanhope Bayne-Jones gave me all manner of helpful advice about the typhoid studies, the weird sequence of the publication, and Vaughan's strange role in the publication of the work.

Col. Robert Joy has been a help in running down many problems and has been a friendly critic as a constant reader over my shoulder, getting me back on the road when I wandered. The same was true of the late Dr. James Bordley. Dr. William Taggert put me on to Walter Reed's contributions concerning labor among Apache women. Dr. Norman Schaftel, in Brooklyn, G.W. Jeffries in Farmville, Virginia; Elmer Lewis Kayser in his history of the Columbian University; Edwin P. Maynard, Jr., for Reed's Brooklyn phase; Vance Nelson of Nebraska; Louis Smith in Murfreesboro, Tennessee; Dr. and Mrs. Owen Wangensteen; Mrs. John Fulton; and many others were helpful and kind.

The following is only a partial list of many others who contributed helping hands; Dr. Daniel L. Borden, Dr. Raymond Brown, Mr. Gilbert J. Clausman, Dr. Wesley Draper, Mrs. John Fulton, Dr. Chalmers Gemmill, Dr. George Gifford, Dr. Hugh G. Grady, Mr. Duncan Groner, Lt. Col. Herbert M. Hart, USMC, Mrs. Spotswood H. Jones, Dr. Saul Jarcho, Mr. Robert H. Kean, Galen L. King, R.P., Dr. John K. Lattimer, Prof. James R. Lucas, Vance E. Nelson, Elmer Parker, Edgar Perry, Mrs. Robert (Sandoz) Pifer, Mr. James C. Reed, Mr. Lemuel Sutton Reed, Dr. Harry S. Shelley, Louis Smith, Dr. Theodore E. Woodward.

Gratitude cannot express my feeling for family assistance, advice, and forbearance, especially to Gail for her enduring tolerance, critical judgment, and affection. She has been in double jeopardy living these many years with two men, Walter Reed and me.

Walter Reed

CHAPTER I

The Matrix

I t was long common in America for parsons' sons to make their mark, and Walter Reed was no exception. One can only wonder whether they inherited from their fathers—and perhaps augmented—an altruistic concern so compelling as to lead to fame, or whether the narrowness and austerity of a Victorian parsonage drove its young inmates to seek their fortunes aggressively in the world.

The cottage in which the last of the Reverend Lemuel Reed's family of five children was born on September 13, 1851, in Gloucester County, Virginia, was not a place in which to tarry, being a temporary home, soon vacated for a proper parsonage in the now vanished town called Belroi. Subsequent assignments from the Methodist Conference took the Reed family to a series of other small Southern towns, including Gatesville and Murfreesboro, North Carolina, and Farmville, Virginia. The children were reared with affection, stern admonitions about duty, readings from the Bible, and a diet dominated by corn-bread. But they read avidly, being fond, like most South-ern youngsters, of Sir Walter Scott and his chivalrous notions that some hold responsible for the Civil War. They worked hard, but their country chores took them out of doors and combined easily with the fun of hunting and the pleasure of being at large in the country teeming with natural bounty.

The four brothers grew strong, and before long were able to tussle with their father in a manly way they all enjoyed. The closely knit family circle remained unbroken until 1859, when the only daughter, Laura, the eldest of the children, married a Methodist minister named James Blincoe.

The beginning of the Civil War turned boys into men. There remains an account of twelve-year-old Walter Reed's being sent with a hired man on a journey of several days in below-zero weather, triumphantly returning with some badly needed money he had been sent to collect. In those days they did not, in today's sense, become teenagers at thirteen or so, but were working hands, responsible for activities necessary for survival. In 1864, after the Reeds had moved to Lawrenceville, they heard that some ma-rauding cavalrymen of Sheridan's were in the neighbor-hood commandeering all the horses they could find. Walter and Christopher Reed, along with a few other boys, tried to hide the horses that provided the family's only means of transportation, and were picked up by a party of raiders and briefly held. Angry at the loss of their horses, the boys would scarcely have believed that Walter Reed would spend most of his adult life in the uniform of the United States Army.

The Civil War was as much of an upheaval for the Reeds as for other Southern families; although few Methodists were affluent enough to own slaves or large plantations, most were devoted to the South in spite of some vehement opposition to slavery. Lemuel Reed, a Whig, often found himself opposed to the wealthier conservatives of the Church of England. His sons Tom and James fought for

The Matrix

the South, James leaving his classes at Randolph-Macon College to join the Liberty Light Artillery. A sergeant by the time Antietam was fought, he lost a hand in that engagement and apparently showed a gallant disregard for what must have been excruciating pain when the shattered member was amputated in a crude field hospital; he is reported to have said to the surgeon, with a bow, "Thank you, Doctor, you have left me enough to hang the girls on." He saw further active duty, and was outraged at Lee's surrender. The poignancy of youthful Southern disappointment appears in an entry in his diary written at twenty-three: "When I arrived home my father said to me: 'well my son, it is all over now.' But I replied: 'No, sir: we will rest up awhile and then we will . . . lick them out of their boots.' But Alas! we never did."

In spite of the disarray in the South after the war, the Methodist Conference was able in 1865 to grant Lemuel Reed's urgent request for assignment to Charlottesville, where the University of Virginia offered the only available opportunity for the education of his four sons. The parsonage was on Ridge Street, near the Virginia Central Railroad tracks on which troops had traveled to Chancellorsville, Manassas, and Wilderness Battlefield, and on which their shattered bodies had been returned to Charlottesville's improvised Confederate Hospital, a warehouse on the site of the present Union Station.

No sooner were the Reeds settled, than Pharaba Reed, that devoted and self-effacing mother, died at age forty-nine. Fourteen-year-old Walter was devastated. On the day of her burial he and his brother Christopher officially joined the Methodist Church, perhaps to keep a promise to her. Her headstone in the graveyard a third of a mile from the parsonage can still be seen. Walter passed it daily on the way to school, and he apparently grieved for her for years, although he threw himself into the work that was to qualify him for the university at fifteen and appeared stoical. In letters written years later he refers to his "poor suffering mother" as "a dear, sainted spirit."

A parson, especially a newly appointed presiding elder

of the district, needed a wife. Before the year was out Lemuel Reed married a wealthy and generous Harrisonburg widow, Mary Catherine Byrd Kyle, whom the children came to love. At the time of the marriage Walter Reed was going to a day school conducted by a Confederate veteran, William Richardson Abbot, and the two years of formal training provided there made up for his earlier educational deficiencies. Abbot, a strong influence on the boy, was a passionate teacher, whose voice rings out of the past with such gems as "Telling is not teaching as hearing is not learning." By the time he graduated from the Abbot School Walter Reed had mastered high-school Latin, Greek, and mathematics, and had learned much from Abbot's wife about art, music, and books.

All the Reed boys except Tom, who hated books, went to the university, but Walter was the only one to graduate. He later reported entering at age sixteen, but he was actually only fifteen; students under sixteen could register if they had older brothers in residence, and Christopher Reed was his younger brother's roommate. The university was itself only fifty years old. Thomas Jefferson had established eight schools, what we would now call departments: schools of Latin, Greek, Natural Philosophy, Natural History, Mathematics, Rhetoric and Written Language, History, and Medicine. For a master's degree the student completed work in all eight, some taking as long as a decade to do so.

The faculty included such distinguished men as Basil Gildersleeve, the Greek professor who was to leave later for the new Johns Hopkins University; William McGuffey, the Presbyterian minister from Cincinnati who taught Moral Philosophy and wrote McGuffey's Reader; and William Wertenbaker, the librarian, who had known Mr. Jefferson well and who allowed Walter to use an alcove as a study. The classrooms and laboratories were in the white-pillared red-brick pavilions on the Lawn, where professors lived with their families. A chairman of the faculty was elected yearly by his colleagues to preside over the university, where the daily schedule was marked by the sound of

The Matrix

the Rotunda bell, faithfully rung by one Henry Martin, who had been a slave of Jefferson's.

It would appear that poverty, sorrow, and a determination to get an education had given Walter Reed little time—and perhaps no inclination—for the carousing that took place at the university, as at most schools for young men. Drinking was never forbidden at the university, and although Edgar Allan Poe was held up as an example of the downfall to which temptations could lead, high spirits were often in evidence, and a bulletproof face had been ordered for the Rotunda clock, a good pistol target. It was in fact the fatal shooting of a distinguished law professor, John Staige Davis, by an exuberant drunken student that brought the Honor Code into being; its requirements seemed only natural to the sober Reed boy, who diligently earned Intermediate Honors in four schools in one year.

It was clearly out of the question for him to make the investment of time and money needed for an M.A. degree, so he applied for admission to the medical school as a candidate for an M.D. He had just turned seventeen. In view of the present requirement of four years of premedical university training before admission to medical school —the completion of which takes another four and is followed by internships and residencies—it is hard to believe that an M.D. could at one time be earned more easily than an M.A. But this was the nineteenth century, and the more recent proliferation of medical knowledge is a story in itself, and one in which twentieth century technology plays a part. Mr. Jefferson had included the department of medicine with the idea that a well-educated man would find medical knowledge useful; the only distinction made between the knowledgable layman and the potential physician was that the latter, to acquire an M.D., had to have a grade of 80 instead of the 75 that was satisfactory for one who had no intention of practicing. Walter Reed did not see a microscope at the university, where they were first introduced by Dr. Dabney in the 1874–75 session. He would first encounter one—as well as

a clinical thermometer—during his studies at Bellevue in
1869. At that time the latter item was a ten-inch rod that
was tucked into the patient's armpit and took five minutes
to register.

The University of Michigan claims to have had the first
full-time medical teaching staff in the country, with five
members by the 1850s, but the University of Virginia had
the first full-time professor of medicine in America—
or elsewhere—by 1825, when Robley Dunglison, then
twenty-five, was persuaded by Jefferson's roving agent,
Francis Gilmer, to come to Charlottesville from England.
He was paid $1500 a year, and a fee of from $25 to $50 for
each student. His practice, except for the patients he saw
at the clinic for teaching purposes, was restricted to
consultation, all fees being turned over to the university.
Nonetheless, he and his family lived comfortably in one of
the handsome pillared pavilions on the Lawn. His practice
then and throughout his subsequent life in Philadelphia
was never large, but he saw four presidents of the United
States in consultation and attended Jefferson in his final
illness, teaching him to catheterize himself.

By the time Walter Reed entered the medical school it
had a graded curriculum, a step-by-step advance from the
basic sciences to clinical art, with laboratories giving ample
opportunity for demonstration. Dunglison insisted on
ten-month sessions, like those of the academic departments, but when Reed entered, a session was only nine
months long. He was a medical student from October 1,
1868, to July 1, 1869.

It was customary for medical schools to concentrate the
teaching of anatomy, then the primary subject, in the
winter months, from around the first of November to the
end of February. Conditions for the care of cadavers were
primitive, largely dependent on cold weather. Moreover,
all dissections were done by daylight; candles or kerosene
lamps gave too little light. Although the dissection amphitheater was the last university building planned by Jefferson, it has been razed. A model of its first phase, super-
vised by Dr. Chalmers Gemill (until recently chairman of

pharmacology), shows that even sunlight was limited by the installation of high fan windows to supplement skylights. A museum on the first floor had a corner known as "the charnel," where residue from dissections was burned.

Medical students were said to be "abundantly provided with fresh subjects," with "ample time . . . for private dissection by daylight," but, reading between the lines, one recalls the zeal of "resurrectionists," who surreptitiously and illegally supplied human bodies for dissection. A Negro janitor was the resurrectionist who brought to the anatomical theater the bodies of executed criminals and the corpses of paupers. It is unclear whether local graveyards were ever violated. A series of elegant colored plates by Henry Scharf was used by the Schools of Anatomy and Physiology to supplement dissection and demonstration.

Most medical schools gave much more time to lectures, and allowed less for actual dissection. Harvard and Columbia offered the same lectures, including theology and history, year after year. At the university of Virginia, fundamental branches of the medical sciences were mastered before their practical application was demonstrated. There were didactic lectures, but also much practical demonstration in the small outpatient teaching clinic. Reed studied chemistry and pharmacy under a man with the marvelous name of Socrates Maupin; medicine (which included legal medicine and obstetrics) under James Harrison; and physiology and surgery under Lawrence Cabell. Dr. John Staige Davis (the son of the murdered law professor) gave instruction in materia medica. Cabell had published in 1859 *The Testimony of Modern Science to the Unity of Mankind*, a book that identified him as a precursor of Darwin, and he became an early advocate of Lister's antiseptic method. Other faculty members in Reed's time were James and C. W. Chancellor, John Lewis, S. S. Neill, Joseph W. Akin, and assistant surgeons James McIntosh, T. A. Michie, M. McKenzie, F. L. Bronaugh, F. M. Letcher, and R. M. Anderson.

We have no record of how the seventeen-year-old boy dealt inwardly with the sights, sounds, and smells of human dissection, but he must have given a satisfactory account of himself. Perhaps his country background, which had involved the care of stock and the trapping and skinning of small animals, was a help. At any rate, he graduated third among the ten in his class of forty-nine earning the M.D., and was the youngest ever to graduate in medicine at the university.

Since the university did not provide much work with patients, in spite of a curriculum more extensive than that of any other American medical school at the time, it was usual for graduates to go on to one of the large hospital medical schools in Baltimore, Philadelphia, New York, or Boston for further training. Walter Reed went to New York's Bellevue. His brother Christopher wanted to study law in New York, so the two went north together, traveling by rail through the ravaged countryside, no doubt uncertain of what awaited them; but the options for young men in those days were few, and young aspirants thought less of the distant future than of the door or two upon which they could knock and, with luck, gain admittance. Both of the Reed brothers were set on a course that they and their family considered honorable, and they sturdily took one step at a time. But as they approached the polyglot metropolis about which they had heard so much, they must have feared, in spite of their unquenchable Southern pride and the knowledge that they were respectably born and well educated for the time, that they might be taken for greenhorns.

Bellevue was a hospital with 1200 beds, an outpatient department, and what it claimed was the only twenty-four hour, hospital-based ambulance service in the world. The ambulance, horse-drawn, was the talk of New York, but Bellevue also claimed other firsts: the first anatomy instruction in the country to use actual dissection (instituted in 1750); the first use of the hypodermic syringe; the first outpatient department (opened in 1867); the first school of nursing, established in 1873 with Florence Nightingale's method; and the first "Emergency Pavilion" (begun in

The Matrix

1876). Bellevue can justly claim to have been the first public hospital in the country, since it originated in 1658 when five workshops of the Dutch West Indies Company were given for hospital use. By 1847 the almshouse section, opened in 1816, was reorganized, and a permanent medical board was established. This made the hospital's resources available for the teaching of medical students at the bedside. Two years later, an amphitheater was built and within the decade a new pathology museum. Thus, well before the formal incorporation of the Bellevue Hospital Medical College (on April 8, 1861), a substantial program of medical education was under way, with reasonably good equipment and space. The most prominent physicians and surgeons of New York were among the professors.

When Walter Reed was listed in Bellevue's 1869–70 catalogue, William Worrall Mayo, the father of the famed Mayo brothers of Minnesota, was included there also. He had briefly worked there after coming from England as an immigrant in 1845 and had returned at age forty-nine, after building a large practice in Rochester, Minnesota, at the time Reed arrived. Dr. Mayo's letters to Rochester, some of which were published in the *Rochester Post*, contain shrewd assessments of the kaleidoscopic and worldly New York scene of that period. They also describe Bellevue as a huge stone structure five stories high, set in a pleasant natural environment and divided into clean and uncrowded specialty wards. But in spite of its scale and innovations, it was full of infection—puerperal fever in obstetrics, and pyemia, erysipelas, and widespread sepsis in surgery.

There were four didactic lectures on every weekday except Saturday during the regular winter session, and students could attend hospital clinical lectures daily. Students bought tickets for special classes—analytical medical chemistry, for example—requiring payment of $25, which included the cost of chemicals. All tickets together came to $140, but students who had attended two full courses of lectures in another accredited medical college could buy all tickets except those for matriculation and dissections for only $70. Private instruction was offered for those who felt the need of it.

There was certainly a great wealth of clinical material, with more than 500 deliveries a year, and an annual overall admission count of 10,000 to 12,000. Contagious patients went to the fever or smallpox hospitals on Blackwell's Island, where the Charity Hospital usually housed a thousand, most of them chronically ill. Among the professors were Alexander Mott, who taught surgical anatomy; B. W. McCready, who taught materia medica and therapeutics; Frank Hamilton and W. H. Van Buren, surgeons; Stephen Smith, who taught surgical anatomy; R. Ogden Doremus, who taught chemistry and toxicology; and Edward Gamaliel Janeway, a wizard at diagnosis of chest diseases, who taught physical diagnosis. Henry Noyes taught diseases of the eye and ear; William Hammond was professor of diseases of the mind and nervous system, and clinical medicine; and Austin Flint, Sr., a member of the famous medical Flint family, taught also, and his son, Austin Flint, Jr., served as secretary to the faculty. Isaac Taylor, professor emeritus of obstetrics, gave clinical lectures, and Fordyce Barker was professor of clinical midwifery. They were all paid little or nothing, earning their living from private practice, to which they devoted much of their time.

For some time Bellevue was under the malign influence of Tammany Hall. Although it eventually managed to cast this off, and new buildings were built and reforms instituted, surgery in the New York of 1869 had not caught up with Lister or with what was being done at other centers. There was a constant struggle with infection and hemorrhage, with dreadfully high mortality. Although crudely administered anesthesia mercifully reduced the pain of an operation, it made it easier to perform one, so infection was given a wider field and claimed more victims. The ambulance system, however, was impressive. London and Paris had a few municipal ambulances, but not under the aegis of a hospital; and New York and Roosevelt hospitals

The Matrix

took eight years to follow Bellevue's example. The ambulance system was based on the experience of the Union Army in the Civil War, and was promoted first by Dr. Hammond, who had been surgeon general of a small army medical corps at the time the war began. Ten ambulances were kept on the alert in the hospital's livery stables, and arrived at a gallup upon notice by telegraph of any disaster or medical crisis. A medical officer would go out with the driver, who had been chosen for his knowledge of New York.

Although his experience in New York introduced the small-town boy from Virginia to the benefits and delights of a great city and gave him an opportunity to mingle with some of its great men, it also put before his young eyes the poverty, illness, and misery that overflowed into one of the world's biggest, bloodiest, and busiest hospitals. Hundreds of thousands of people were pouring into a country that had no restrictions on immigration. Some of the "masses yearning to be free" came to the land of opportunity only to suffer. There were no "programs" of welcoming care for the poor, and Reed's young idealism was painfully challenged by the widespread filth, despair, and agony.

Since he got credit for some of the basic science courses he had taken at the university, Reed could concentrate at Bellevue on clinical work. In December 1869, when just eighteen, he took the competitive examination for the position of assistant physician at the Infants', or Nursery, Hospital at Randall's Island, and ranked first. He assumed his new position in January, continuing to take some courses, but his M.D. degree from Bellevue was withheld until he became twenty-one.

The Infants' Hospital had been founded in 1854 by wealthy matrons concerned about the infants of women who served as wet nurses, for dreadful tales were told about the plight of the women and their own children. It had 450 beds, with patients suffering from tuberculosis, syphilis, inanition, colitis, and pneumonia, and with fatalities approaching one out of every three admissions. A considerable amount of spirits was routinely used, some to sedate the infants, no doubt, but more to cajole workers to stay on at a job where they earned little or nothing.

Apparently society has long thought it appropriate to put the unemployed to work caring for the sick, although nowadays they are paid competitive wages, a situation that would (perhaps) gratify the hospital's house physician, who bore the proud Harvard name of Dunster. Dr. Dunster begged the Commissioners of Public Charities and Corrections to do something about the "staffing" of his hospital with "society's derelicts." "I believe," he wrote, "that the whole system of caring for orphans and found-ling infants by relying upon free labor is vicious . . . that eventually we must pay as freely . . . for the care of these helpless little ones as we now pay for the care of our domestic animals." He was perhaps unduly sanguine when he promised that "If such a system could be introduced here the neglect of duty and sullenness of disposition . . . could be done away with immediately." The situation should be seen in the context of the poor pay given physicians in that period, some earning no more than $150 a year. An estimate offered the Commissioners of Public Charities in 1870 indicated that in "relapsing and fever hospitals" doctors were paid $8.00 a week and nurses the same amount per month.

Walter Reed's next appointment could not have lifted his spirits very much, although it introduced him to wider fields of medical practice in which there was great variety of clinical material. Kings County Hospital, Brooklyn, where he worked for four months in 1871, was connected with the County Farm, a resource for the penniless sick. Its crowds of geriatric and chronic patients acquainted him with rock-bottom abdication from human dignity. He must have felt considerable relief when he was offered a residency at Brooklyn City Hospital, which emphasized orthopedics. There he remained until August 1872, com-ing under the influence of a Virginia-born physician, Dr. A. N. Bell, who was deeply concerned with problems of community health and sanitation, campaigning for, among other measures, the sterilization of rags imported

The Matrix

from all over the world for making paper. It may very well have been Dr. Bell who turned Reed's attention for the first time away from the bedside to the possibilities of fighting plagues by preventive action, the relevance of which might not be apparent—or even acceptable—to the general public. Bell was convinced that yellow fever was infectious, but not contagious, and boasted of having stopped an epidemic on a ship during the Mexican War by using steam as a disinfectant. He did not, however, anticipate Reed's intuition about the transmission of the disease by mosquitoes, and, indeed, through a sad quirk of fate, was later to attack bitterly his erstwhile student's brilliant presentation at the 1901 meeting of the American Public Health Association, clinging to his old notion of transmission by contaminated material.

The Brooklyn Board of Health had been organized for several years when Walter Reed was appointed assistant sanitary officer at the ripe old age of twenty-two. He was also made a member of the Medical Society of the County of Kings, and thus plunged into further consideration of sanitary disease control, since the society was pressing for a mandatory drainage law. His emergence into medical circles beyond those of a hospital ward did not, however, make him more hopeful about his career. He felt not only that he was making little progress, and that he was a very young and vulnerable man without influential backing, but that he was losing most of the illusions he had had about the practice of medicine. The art of medicine as practiced at the Brooklyn hospitals was generally poor, and he was surrounded by cuppers and bleeders, badly educated men who nonetheless went unchallenged and waxed fat and prosperous. As district physician in one of the worst sections of the boom town run by Boss Tweed, he was aghast at the injustice of paying honor to physicians who lacked scientific knowledge or diagnostic skill, and at their own indifference to their shortcomings—if, indeed, they ever acknowledged having any.

His brother Christopher wrote of finding Walter depressed by a doctor's report of the death of a child patient.

WALTER REED

The doctor had come to Reed finely dressed and conveyed by a splendid carriage with coachman and footman in attendance. But when he gave the required official information about the death "He was so *ignorant* that he couldn't *use correctly medical nomenclature* . . . [or] state its symptoms." Reed went on to tell his brother that his visitor had given a Latin name *backwards*, but that he had the leading practice in the area in spite of being a "first class quack." "I shall quit the profession!" he cried in disgust, but Christopher succeeded in mollifying him for the moment.

The young doctor was not only suffering from keen disillusionment; he was trying to make his way in the midst of a catastrophic economic depression to which speculation in the Northern Pacific Railroad and overexpansion in industry and agriculture had contributed. According to Christopher, after returning from a medical meeting one night Walter stood for a while looking down from his window at the great city, and said slowly as though no one heard him, "Woe unto thee, Chorazin, woe unto thee, Bethsaida, for if the mighty works which were done in you had been done in Tyre and Sidon, they would long ago have repented in sack cloth and ashes," whereupon he knelt by his bed and said the Lord's Prayer with great feeling.

The classic reaction to such despair is to get into trouble, especially when one is young. Walter Reed then got into trouble in an entirely uncharacteristic way. In his fifth year in New York he lived in what today is the Williamsburg section of Brooklyn, in the Nineteenth Ward, where a third of the population were recent immigrants, mostly Germans. The assimilation of these "Dutchmen," as they were scornfully called, was not being accomplished altogether peaceably, and Reed somehow got into a squabble with a German fellow boarder that led to blows and police intervention. Calling himself contritely a "hot-headed Virginian," Reed claimed that he had been slandered in a way that would have brought about a duel in an earlier day, but that in retrospect he had to admit could do him no harm.

The Matrix

The situation must have been all the more vexing for him because both his landlady and his boss, Dr. Segur, sided with the German, a man from the customs house named Kedzie. It may have become clear to Reed that Segur's intervention was made in a fatherly way, introducing the voice of reason, since he continued to work under Segur's supervision for another year.

The classic solution for a young man feeling sorry for himself is to fall in love, and before long Walter Reed did just that. On a visit to his family in Murfreesboro, North Carolina, in 1874, his eye was taken by a young girl in church named Emily Lawrence (although she called herself Emilie to be more elegant). She had in fact been there for a long time, having been born across the street from the Reeds when Walter was six years old, but now the time was ripe for the young doctor to go through the throes and joys of what seems to have been his first—and only—love. After a few amusingly stilted letters to her, he began the voluminous correspondence with her he was to conduct for the rest of his life whenever they were apart—as, of necessity, they often were. An early letter mentions for the first time his plan to enter the Army Medical Corps, and shares his painful awareness of being young and unsponsored and his hope that the army would offer maturing travel.

It was necessary to pass examinations to enter the Army—examinations lasting for five hours a day for six successive days, covering Latin, Greek, mathematics, and history besides medicine, in addition to which, members of the examining board could go further afield with any question they fancied about Shakespeare, engineering, anthropology, or archeology. He found it immensely difficult to return to habits of study, and his apprehension was not abated on learning that 500 candidates would complete for fewer than 30 vacancies in the small medical corps. The examination he was to take was set for late in the year 1874, and he did not know in advance that it would blessedly be postponed until January 18, 1875. Thus, he was for a number of months under the pressure of preparing himself while at the same time continuing to discharge his heavy responsibilities for the health of Brooklyn, and it is perhaps not surprising that he fell ill toward the end of August with a prostrating but unspecified disorder that lasted three weeks. It may or may not have been helpful to him during this period to hear often from Emilie, who seems to have been using the ploy any such young girl not formally bespoken might use —reporting to the point of fantasy the pleasures of her daily social life without him.

Although his letters were no less full of fantasy, all directed toward her charms, he was able to alter his writing style sufficiently to work up the first detailed record of the Fifth Sanitary District for the *Report of the Health of the City of Brooklyn,* in which he conveyed his concern over the problems incidental to the haphazard growth of New York City and Brooklyn from a cluster of small towns into a largely unplanned megalopolis. He noted that those who could leave the city in the summertime did so, and bluntly pointed out that the city's stench, though somewhat less noxious in the winter, was always noticeable, and could be detected even on the grand boulevards. Parts of the Nineteenth Ward were just a few feet above tide level, and since engineers did not know or care about natural drainage, there was much malaria.

He knew that the Common Council would do nothing about recommendations of the City Health Officer concerning filling, grading, and drainage problems. Garbage collectors used any vacant lot for a dump. But he wistfully pointed out that in many sections the draining of ponds reduced the incidence of malaria, and that zealous and continual inspection of streets and tenements was the only way to improve the environment and make it not only more bearable but more healthful. Those who pine for the good old days are reminded that, in addition to ubiquitous garbage and sewage, city dwellers had to deal with the product of the stabling of an enormous number of horses within the city proper. No attention whatever would be paid to all such nuisances, with their potential for sickness

The Matrix

and death, he felt, unless "some authority, such as that of the Board of Health, is brought to bear on this population." He further inveighed against the public schools, calling them "great 'hot beds' for the dissemination of such diseases as measles, scarletina, and perhaps diphtheria" because too little vigilance was used in readmitting children not yet recovered from these diseases.

The passionate crusader against pestilence may have been unaware of his destiny in that winter of 1874, but by then he was taking his first hesitant steps toward it.

CHAPTER II

In the Medical Corps,
for Better or for Worse

In spite of his misgivings, Doctor Reed was entirely successful in handling the Army Medical Corps examination that made him in 1875 an officially appointed assistant surgeon and first lieutenant in the United States Army at the age of twenty-four. A look at his qualifying papers shows that he answered questions on the anatomy of the throat, for example, more precisely than could most anatomy instructors today unless they had specialized in a nose and throat department. But he did equally well when it came to discussing yellow fever, questions about which made up the whole hygiene section of the examination.

He knew, for instance, that the fever was endemic in such places as Cuba, British Guiana, Louisiana, Santa Domingo, Haiti, and the coast of Peru, with special concentration in such cities as Havana, Demerara, and New Orleans. He considered it transmissible "either by germs clinging to clothing or in the cargo of a ship—or by a person, who is at the time sick of the disease being transported to a non-infected locality," but he noted that its propagation in a new locality depended on heat, moisture, and, in all likelihood, sanitary conditions. He was aware that it seldom appeared above 40° north and that a cold snap was likely to check its course. He pointed with satisfaction to the reduction of the disease in New Orleans when that city was under military law. He quoted the generally accepted views of the medical community of the time that quarantine helped prevent introduction of the disease, especially the quarantine of infected ships, and that the disinfection of "infected clothing" was useful. Although the typhoid bacillus would not be discovered by Eberth for another five years, the young examinee speculated about "a close connection between pollution of water with fecal matter & causation of typhoid fever," noting that the disease was "generally held to be contagious."

Even while relaxing with satisfaction over his success at passing the examination, Reed was chastened by a note from the president of the examining board that "respectfully recommended that Dr. Reed be admonished that his acquaintance with general literature and science was not up to the expected standard, and that he will be required to make up the deficiency before his second examination." Perhaps this rather haughty criticism lay behind his lifelong effort to teach himself French, which caused him considerable difficulty.

Before casting his lot with the military, he had a chance to make a few visits to Murfreesboro to plead his case with Emilie Lawrence. One letter written between visits was composed with an air of mature wisdom beguiling in a man of twenty-four: "During the past 6 years I have seen something of the affection which men and women bear toward one another; (God knows, I must confess that I have witnessed its absence more than its presence;) . . . during these years I have given much thought to this subject; . . . living in the largest city in America, I have seen & met the most fascinating women; and yet need I

In the Medical Corps

tell you & *you alone* are the only woman whom I have admired!"

The first letter with definite reference to their being engaged is dated June 1, 1875. Walter's stepmother had invited his fiancée to visit her when Walter should be there, and the proposal filled him with alarm at the opportunities it would make for "the people of Murfrees-boro" to believe that such a visit expressed "a silly desire to see me!" One is obliged to wonder whether he was reluctant to have his fiancée "talked about" or was simply too shy to face his beloved with equanimity in a household of curious relatives.

Perhaps it was natural for him to feel uncomfortably, if proudly, conspicuous, for he was having to get accustomed to a flamboyant uniform. For Reed's rank, army regulations specified dress uniform of a dark blue coat, with trousers of a lighter shade of blue, trimmed with emerald green piped in white. A picture taken in Harrisonburg in June shows the newly qualified officer posed rather stiffly in formidable military stance, his left hand resting uneasily on his new sword, of which he was enormously proud. At that time, high-ranking officers, particularly those fighting the Indians, could dress according to their wildest fancy, but the garrison officer dressed strictly according to protocol, which, incidentally, had nothing to do with the weather.

The examination had enabled Walter Reed to renew his acquaintance with George Torney, a classmate in medical school, who also took it. Torney had gone into the navy, but after three years of trying to conquer an unconquerable propensity to seasickness, he entered the army instead, becoming a great crony of Walter Reed's. The new boy was quick to make inquiries of one with more military experience regarding his chances of getting time off to marry Emilie. The advice he got offered limited encouragement, Torney saying that "he only knew that in the Navy it was not easy for a young officer to obtain leave of absence very soon after entering the service, but that it was the invariable custom to grant a leave to a man for the purpose of *getting married!*" Reed must have done considerable tossing and turning before going to sleep each night, not only anticipating married life but thinking of the thousand practical considerations that had suddenly become his. He still had to buy an engagement ring and seems to have had as little idea of how to go about this as he had money with which to purchase it.

He was, however, pleased with his first military assignment—temporary duty at Willet's Point, New York Harbor—although he began longing for Emilie before his train pulled out of the depot on July 23. He wrote to her from the train, and he wrote to her again, within a few hours, from the steamer *Georgiana*. He always suffered from violent seasickness, so it must have been hard for him to produce a romantic letter with a broken stub of a pencil while on a pitching ship. A more legible but similarly lovelorn letter written on July 29 told Emilie that he found Willet's Point an attractive place. He described it for her in great detail, expatiating on the natural beauty of the post and confiding that he had been told "it is regarded as one of the most desirable posts in the Service," and that indeed he "would like to remain several years."

He seems to have enjoyed from the beginning the amenities of post life—the orderly sick call (with few patients); the "agreeable gentlemen" of his mess; riding in a horse-drawn buggy with a fellow officer; and watching the parade every evening, which took place to the music of "an excellent band." "I have become quite used to my Military Clothing," he wrote Emilie with satisfaction, "and feel just like an old soldier. Have an abundance of time reading & have already got well to work."

His caseload was light because the post was "decidedly a healthy one"—without the problems of malaria, typhoid, and other ailments all too common in those days wherever troops were concentrated. And the post hospital was described by the famous Dr. John Shaw Billings as "the best post hospital that I know of. . . . In location, solidity and thoroughness of construction, convenience of administration and in the amount of ventilation of the wards it is

In the Medical Corps

not surpassed by any Army hospital." Nearly twelve acres were devoted to gardens, and hospital attendants and convalescent patients cultivated a vegetable garden. The post had its own chapel, library, fire department, and printing offices, and the men had a literary and dramatic club, a billiard room, and a bowling alley, and were allowed to give dances in the mess hall.

It was no doubt fortunate for Reed that conditions in his first post allowed him to be sanguine about married life in the military, for apparently his fiancée was beginning to have second thoughts about the hardships her marriage was likely to entail. He was able to urge her in good conscience not "to let them talk to you, as if you were taking upon yourself the life of a slave! As if you were resigning friends, comforts, and happiness! As if you were going to live forever upon the borders of Civilization & never enjoy enlightened society! As if you were joining yourself to a man who can't provide subsistence for you and of whom you should be ashamed!"

Apparently Emilie had not simply been disturbed over what she heard about life in the military; another suitor was on the horizon—or at least so she claimed—one who was well-to-do and came from Baltimore. Perhaps her repeated mention of him was at least in part a maneuver to advance her wedding plans. It led her fiancé to declare himself "a miserable mortal . . . to have been born poor," in any case. But after she had solemnly reproved him for reproving her for her interest in another man, Reed's declaration that "my only happiness in life is in your love" prevailed.

Had Reed been assigned first to an *average* military hospital he might have lacked the temerity to persist in his courtship. Post hospitals of the period were often temporary buildings, heated by stoves or fireplaces and lighted by kerosene lamps and candles, in which casuals in the army and hospital stewards nursed the sick. Some of the more ambitious of these stewards went into medical school and became army physicians. The routine work of caring for the sick or working as a pharmacist, orderly, or wardmaster fell to the lot of privates, who generally disliked such duty in spite of extra pay. Since the auxiliary staff was detached from the line, it was only partly under the surgeon's control; mismanagement, cruelty, neglect, even subtle attack could not be punished by the post surgeon without the backing of the post commander. An occasional post commander smart enough to realize that his success depended on the health of his troops might cooperate, but since the physician had no command function and was held in less esteem, in spite of his education, it took diplomacy to keep things running smoothly. The post surgeon treated sick soldiers and officers and their families as well as civilian employees, who sometimes outnumbered the military. Usually, the army doctor was the only one available for dozens or hundreds of miles, and he took the best care he could of anyone who needed medical help. He was also responsible for seeing that the food and water used were safe, the quarters sanitary, and the drainage systems working. But the doctor's monthly sanitary reports could reach the surgeon general only if the post commander forwarded them, and before 1885, when new regulations were put into effect, he threw them away as often as not, doing nothing about their recommendations.

But it probably would have been beside the point to go into all this with Emilie in any case, for when Reed's orders came, on April 8, 1876, they were for Yuma, California. At that time, going into the trackless Indian country was like going to the moon. Overwhelmed with dismay, Reed consulted someone in New York or Washington about an arrangement for leave while in Arizona so he could get married, only to be told, according to Emilie's reminiscences, "Young man, if you don't want to go to Arizona, resign from the Service." When Reed stoutly answered that he had not labored for his commission only to give it up "so hastily," the general (whose identity has never been altogether clear) advised him to postpone his marriage until some soldier in Arizona might go mad and have to be escorted east by a medical officer. That this was an

In the Medical Corps

idiotic—or simply evasive—suggestion was borne out by the fact that Reed never had this duty until thirteen years later, when he did indeed take a patient from Alabama to St. Elizabeth's in Washington. So he wrote Emilie that since it appeared that he would have to remain in Arizona for three or four years, they must marry at once. And they did, on April 26, 1876, in Murfreesboro.

Two weeks later they parted, the groom having with great reluctance decided to go alone and arrange for his bride to join him in the fall. He himself had no choice but to go, and he wanted to see for himself what his new post was like and to find out the best way to make the journey before taking her on what was sure to be at best a rocky road.

Yuma was considered a hellhole because of its excessive heat and trackless dust. The surgeon general's 1870 report on Fort Yuma called it "well selected as a defense against the Indians," but added that it would be "impossible to find a more uninviting spot . . . than this small promontory of decomposing trachyte," and that "The air was so dry that sweat evaporated before it could be felt," and "Furniture falls to pieces; traveling chests gap at their seams." Dehydration caused stores to shrink; even eggs dried out, and other supplies lost appreciable weight. Daily temperatures of 113° F. seem to have been the rule. A man who would go there after a journey that took nearly a month by boat, railroad, stagecoach, and army wagon, leaving a new bride behind, simply to discharge a newly assumed duty would have trouble adjusting to the world of today. Present-day physician recruitment notices stress the comfort of the situation needing a new man, the high salary offered, the benefits, and often the ready access to outdoor sports. To be fair, it must be allowed that the outdoor sports that awaited Walter Reed in the West, such as fishing and riding, were free.

During the second week in August Reed was sent from the fire into the frying pan, to Camp Lowell on the outskirts of Tucson, where temperature ranges from 110° to 115° in the shade. It was Apache country, and the

surgeon general's report spoke of a detachment of Apache
scouts who lived half a mile from the post as being "very
liable to attacks of pulmonary disease on exposure during
the winter." It was no doubt consoling to those at Camp
Lowell to read further that "the Apaches who murder and
plunder on the roads radiating from Tucson dwell in the
more northern mountain ranges." The Papago Indians, of
whom there were also many, were described as "friendly to
the whites and peaceable in their character, occupying
themselves in raising corn and melons." The report refers
further to the post garden's production of superlative
vegetables—in season, and with painstaking irrigation.
Because of the immense distances, the cost of importing
food was appalling—butter was $2.00 a pound, and eggs
were $1.00 a dozen.

Medical care was needed not only for sunstroke but for
gastrointestinal complaints and considerable venereal disease and alcoholism, the latter being held reasonably in
check by the logistics of importing liquor for sale to men
who were poorly paid. Nearby Tucson, the territory's capital, was a rowdy town notorious for more than a century, with about 3,200 inhabitants, mostly Spanish-speaking.
The mail came twice a week, via San Diego and the mail
stage through Yuma. Boredom, along with the excessive
midday heat, was pervasive in the self-contained village
that was Tucson, which was several miles to the west of Fort
Lowell. Dr. Reed began to worry about malaria, ascribing
its incidence partly to the wide daily swings in temperature. Most of the men bunked in tents, with no bathing
facilities. Adobe structures such as the new hospital had an
adobe roof and were cooler. They leaked when it rained,
however—which it did sometimes, even in the territory
—and the men had to pitch tents indoors to keep the rain
off their beds.

Emilie's girlhood had been comfortable and sheltered.
It was undoubtedly the most courageous act of her life
when she took off from Virginia for San Francisco,
surviving some kind of train wreck en route. It may well
have been the bravest act of Walter Reed's life, which

In the Medical Corps

included many brave acts, for him to bring his wife to the wild west. Perhaps the fierce mustache that he had grown during their separation, and wore when he met her in the Palace Hotel, was an unconscious gesture of self-protection on his part, for by now he knew that some of the "horrows" of army life, as she had girlishly called them, would be impossible to ignore. They met on November 5, "after six months of sighs and tears and protestations that no other human beings were ever so cruelly dealt with." One salutes the tenacity and optimism of first love.

They spent two weeks in San Francisco, where we can hope that their joy at being together again was sufficient to make up for the vicissitudes already undergone—and those yet to come. Then they went by steamer to San Diego on what, in view of the groom's propensity for seasickness, we can only hope were truly pacific waters. The ensuing 500-mile journey in what Reed grandly refers to as "a private conveyance" but which was very likely the usual army ambulance drawn by mules, was a nightmare. It took twenty-three days, and they camped out at night en route. One letter Reed wrote about the trip reports that his wife spent some nights in terror and tears, and that when he was not at her side she would call out into the darkness, "Where are you, Dr. Reed?" Since, according to the custom of the time, she never called her husband anything else, this account has a stronger ring of truth than one might at first suppose, but it is, of course, possible that he wrote it to tease her, and read it to her with an attempt at conciliation before sending it.

By five o'clock on the first day, they had made no more than ten miles; Reed had to walk the team. By seven it was cold, and the moonless night completely opaque. Reed noted of his weeping wife, "I must give her credit for great bravery on this, her first night in an ambulance," and added, "I'm afraid if there had been a stone wall nearby I should have brought my head in violent contact with it." But they plodded on through the dark over a road so rough that it seemed at times as though the ambulance would overturn. About eleven they came on a small camp, where they were told that the station that was their destination was two miles away, "over the worse road in California" (*sic*). The trail on which they had to travel lay between steep hills that they felt rather than saw. The mules balked at picking their way through the rocks. Reed wrote an account of their further approach to the station:

> Fortunately the driver had a lantern and part of a candle. This we lit, and taking with me a soldier who was riding with the driver, I started ahead to show the way. By keeping just in front of the team and holoaing . . . we managed to make some progress. Poor E. all this time was . . . calling out continually, "Where are you, Dr. Reed? Please come back and let the soldier carry the lantern," but I told her I could trust no man living to point the way out of this horrible canon [*sic*]; and on I went in sand nearly up to my knees, calling to the driver. . . . Notwithstanding the very great advantage of the lantern . . . and an excellent driver, every fifty yards would find a wheel stopped by some great boulder.

The station was reached a little after midnight—a small house about ten feet square, with a stable.

> As soon as Emilie got within doors and saw the bright fire, her spirits rose accordingly and when the tea was ready . . . her humour was of the best. All her sprightliness returned and as she took a glance around the room . . . she laughed heartily, and declared that she wouldn't take anything for this experience . . . The "bed" was especially an object of much merriment. . . . She declared that she could never rest on such a contrivance; but when I had arranged things a little, had spread over the piece of canvas a blanket . . . and had drawn my overcoats over us, we both soon fell asleep and did not wake till broad daylight. Thus passed Emilie's first day and night on her trip to Fort Lowell!

For the reconstruction of the young couple's life at Fort Lowell we must depend largely on the careful ledger Walter kept, since it was no longer necessary for him to pour out his heart in letters. The account books of that

In the Medical Corps

period were not incidental to their lives, but at the heart of it because of the always meager appropriations made by Congress for the military; these had been declining throughout the 1870s and fell to zero in 1877. Not until November 30 of that year did any money become available; for the first eleven months of 1877 everyone in the army had to depend on family dole, loans from usurious bankers, or money earned in some kind of moonlighting activity. No doubt the final convulsive spasm of the occupying forces of the Reconstruction, and the hope of Southern congressmen that they could be starved out, had something to do with this incredibly low point in the story of the U.S. Army. Congressional neglect of the army was neither a regional nor a seasonal phenomenon, however, but one reflecting a common peacetime attitude.

Since a haircut cost fifty cents, Walter could only afford such a luxury at intervals of from six weeks to five months, and it took more than a quarter of a month's pay to keep a Chinese cook. The young husband was obviously doing all he could to make life easy for his wife. It was perhaps Valentine's Day that inspired a February entry for "7 yards edging, two blocks Ribbon ($1.50), 3 yards calico, 17 yards lace @ 50 cents." He had had to borrow from his father to survive the payless period, and he may have had some help also from Emilie's relatives. Things were a bit easier in April, and the couple indulged themselves in six slides for their stereopticon, which might be thought of as a very primitive precursor of the television.

By spring Emilie was pregnant, and during July the Reeds—having been assigned to Camp Apache, a relatively new camp in the heart of the White Mountain Apache Reservation—had to undertake another journey of roughly 200 miles that repeated the hardships of their first experience in western travel. They went in the company of several men, with a goodly number of mules and horses. Each day's stint had to be planned according to where water could be found in that arid country. Emilie took along a dog for company, and a basket that contained her "work"—embroidery, no doubt—and four novels, among many other things. Two hats, a sword, an umbrella, a pair of shoes, a carbine, a pistol, a cartridge belt, and two full canteens hung from the roof of the wagon. It is hard to see how Emilie's pregnancy survived the trip, particularly its last day, which took them out of a pretty green valley through which they had been making their way earlier, to passage through a canyon that Reed claimed was "simply beyond language" to describe. On the *good* part of the canyon road, he explained, "the wheels jump from rock to rock with perfect *crash* at times." From ten in the morning until five o'clock the caravan made thirty feet, by actual measurement; then the path was so steep that it was necessary to lock the wheels of the ambulance and drag a large tree behind it to keep the vehicle from going end over end. At length they reached a complete break in the road, a "sheer descent of five feet, right over the face of a rock." "Every man braces himself for the struggle," Reed wrote. "We pause a moment and then are jerked full twenty feet right over the rocks! So sudden was the leap and with such terrible force did I strike the ground that the very soles of my shoes were torn off!"

Perhaps, had the eleven-day journey been easier, the travelers would have had time to worry about the very real threat of hostile Indians. It was reported (to Emilie's horror) after they had arrived safely, that one of their stopping places had been the scene of a bloody battle between two tribes only three days after their passage; these were the days of Geronimo. But the young wife had no reason to fear her husband's Indian patients, who —although they often summoned the medicine man to back up the white doctor—acknowledged the good that Reed accomplished for them and were grateful. Emilie wrote that they were very fond of him, and often brought a haunch of venison as a present. She must have had strong nerves by then, for she noted that "If no one was in the house to receive it they would walk stealthily in and lay it on [my] white muslin dressing table, or take a picture from the wall and hang it there."

It was a good thing that the Indians felt the need to pay

their doctor, for the United States government, asked to add something to Reed's pay for his extra work with the Indians, refused. A report made to the Committee on Military Affairs in 1882 tried again to have "pay allowed by law for discharging the duties of a physician to the White Mountain Apache Indians," noting that Reed had indeed "rendered valuable professional services to the Indians." The senators pondering the case pointed to an 1839 law forbidding any extra pay for any "officer in any branch of the public service," and again denied the bill developed by others on Reed's behalf. It was simply not in the cards for Walter Reed to even sit on the fringes of prosperity. Simple solvency seemed to elude him, although the account book he kept crows triumphantly that on December 30, 1877, he had paid off all outstanding debt, his total expenses for the year having been kept to $1,178.00!

It was fortunate that by the time Emilie came to term, a good new hospital had been built at Apache. When the post had been established in 1870, it was considered temporary. In any case, lumber was in short supply and the early buildings were open to the sky, with canvas ceilings that leaked whenever it rained. The summers were warm and wet from June into the winter, and snowstorms, at an elevation of 6,000 feet, could be expected in April.

Walter Reed must have delivered his own son, born on December 4, 1877, since he was the only doctor for 200 miles. The labor must have been difficult for both parents, for a letter he wrote two years later points to pain and guilt scarcely concealed by the curious third-person style of disclosure customary in that time and a reticence about emotional issues quite foreign to people today. "Papa remembers how sick his poor sweet wife was & how patiently she bore it all, and remembering this, he could never see his precious brought to bed again, except it should be her own wish! Now, darling, it isn't *every* husband who is so thoughtful of his wife's welfare, & who for her sake, would have made such a promise."

Lawrence Reed's first year or so of life seems, nevertheless, to have given great satisfaction to his parents, who

WALTER REED

settled down to a fairly pleasant existence at Apache. And there was another addition to the family—an Indian girl named Susie, four or five years old, who had been so badly burned in some Indian fracas that she had been abandoned. After treating her burns Reed took her home with him, and she helped care for his children for some fifteen years.

When his son was little more than a year old, Reed was given a forty-five day leave to take him, with his mother, to the railroad in New Mexico for a trip home to Virginia. Although his letters to Emilie after her departure betray a kind of baffled sadness, he described his mess at Apache as being "very jolly," and he clearly came to enjoy the resumption of his life as a man among men, gaining a reputation for being a great "wag and joker." He spent much time with Dorsey McPherson, a close friend who was his junior by six years; the two men went fishing, held shooting matches, hunted, studied—and worked, with one eye on Geronimo and other Indians. A letter of Reed's written in May told Emilie about going to San Carlos to enlist Indian scouts, a trip that soured him forever on field service.

Apparently both he and Emilie had expected to be reunited after a separation of only a few months, but he failed to get the transfer he wanted, and he overcame his wife's pleas to be allowed to return by pointing out the expense and impracticality of such a move, since his assignment was sure to change before much longer. With McPherson he spent Christmas on a rugged ten-day hunting trip. On his return to camp he found a letter from his wife telling of a dangerous illness that his son had undergone, but from which he was making a good recovery.

A summary of his service at Apache, from August 1877 to May 1880, when he was relieved to go to Richmond, indicate that a third of his patients had infections, a fifth of which were venereal, and a third had injuries. About 6 percent suffered from alcoholism and from gastrointestinal, neurological, and psychological disorders. There were

In the Medical Corps

many respiratory problems, and problems of the eyes and skin. It was while he was at Apache that he contributed information about Apache obstetrical practices to three articles by George J. Engelmann of St. Louis, published in the *Transactions of the American Gynecological Society.* This seems to have been the first appearance of his name in medical "literature." But it was not his last.

When his orders came, and he could set his eyes eastward, he celebrated by buying a box of Pear's soap for a dollar, a new pair of shoes, and two pairs of white gloves. He took little Susie with him.

CHAPTER III

The Plateau

Until he returned to the West in December 1882, going to a post at Fort Omaha, Doctor Reed's career was rather pleasantly sidetracked. He had been made a captain in June 1880. After a joyous reunion with his family, he had time to have a portrait of Lawrence painted (by Richard Norris Brooks, who charged fifty dollars for it) before being sent to a sinecure job at Fort Ontario, Oswego, New York, where his caseload consisted of five patients in as many months. One soldier had only a sprained ankle.

His next assignment, taking him to Fort McHenry in Baltimore, in February 1881, allowed the Reed family to live in considerable comfort in the Carrollton Hotel, renowned for its cuisine. Walter Reed wrote to his friend McPherson that this duty "suited him to a dot" and was "several 'pegs' higher than I had ever aspired." Assignment to Washington Barracks, which came soon, did not put an end to the Reeds' being more in the swim than they

had ever felt; Reed had the sober duty of guarding
Charles Guiteau, Garfield's assassin, during the time he
was in custody at Washington's police headquarters, but
the next month he was part of a splendid celebration in
Yorktown, which brought together the political elite of the
country to mark the centennial of Cornwallis's surrender.

The next year, 1882, the Reeds were stationed at Fort
Omaha, where the major problem was a continual battle
with the bureaucracy to improve the sanitary conditions of
the post. Here the Reeds' only daughter, Emily, was born.
She was known through most of her life as Blossom Reed.
Two months after her birth he was made surgeon-in-
charge of Fort Sidney, Nebraska. His family responsibilities seemed to be compounding, for his brother Tom was
severely hurt in an accident at a Fourth of July celebration
in Kansas and had to have a hand amputated—as his
brother James had, many years earlier. He was not doing
well, and needed Walter for his medical skill as well as for
his loving support. Tom Reed, who seems to have been
victimized in a business venture by an absconding partner,
had tried homesteading. He had a number of children,
one of whom tried to help when her uncle dressed her
father's wound, although she was only seven. When she
fainted, her Uncle Walter consoled her—and took her
home with him when he left, having helped his brother
onto the road to recovery. As an old lady Sallie left an
account of her journey with him back to Sidney that gives
a beguiling picture of both of them, the little girl full of
awe at the train and all the sights, and an uncle lovingly
enjoying her wonder. But the child was incurably home-
sick, and soon had to be put back on a train alone, with a
huge placard around her neck bearing her name and
address, as though she were a letter.

During the same year, in having to deny a request for
money from his sister Laura, who now had ten children
and very little money, Walter Reed accounted accurately
for his inability to comply by mentioning, among other
obligations and expenses, loans he had already made to
two of his brothers, and a debt he owed his father. The

The Plateau

household at Fort Sidney was in any case not a happy one at this point. Emilie was not well, and her husband was worried and extremely busy. He had found that being surgeon-in-charge was much more difficult than being an assistant to the surgeon. He inherited problems in the medical service in what was still a hell-raising railroad town. His predecessor had been desperate about recurrent battles with cases of fevers—remittent, intermittent, and typhoidal. Reed wrestled with the same problems, and things seemed to be particularly bad in the harsh winter of 1883, when an outbreak of erysipelas gave him experience that he would later report in his first original scientific paper. But by August 1884 he was sent off again by the army, this time to Fort Robinson, in the panhandle of Nebraska.

He was successful in putting together the badly crushed ankle of one of his first patients, an eighteen-year-old Swiss immigrant who had been battling with homesteaders against the ranchers of the region when he had a bad fall into a seventy-foot well and landed on his heel. Confusingly, the youth was known as "Old Jules," and in time a book of that title by his daughter, Mari Sandoz, became a Book-of-the-Month-Club best-seller, long after all the principals were dead.

Emilie Reed hated the dry sandhill country. Since the government was feeding the Indians in 1884, the Red Cloud Agency issuing rations to 11,000–12,000 Indians every ten days, they were no longer so aggressive, but there were other things to worry about. The hospital had burned down, and patients had to be cared for in tents until the new building was completed in 1885. Still, the Reeds' own house was a two-story adobe dwelling with a large screened veranda and pleasantly landscaped grounds. Faced with clapboard, it today offers (along with other such houses on the old post) inviting accommodations for tourists.

Things *were* getting civilized. Just how advanced they were in 1884 is a little hard to determine, although an army wife named Ellen Biddle, who lived at Fort Robinson

WALTER REED

three years after the Reeds' departure, has left us a
glowing account of dinner parties there, where "you would
not have known you were not in Washington, . . . the silver,
glass and china were so beautiful." She added, "The life
here was very pleasant; the quarters were excellent, and
with good plumbing, the first I had seen in the army."
Possibly three years had brought about great change—or
possibly Emilie Reed reacted to her environment out of her
own unhappiness.

Emilie Reed's account of an episode from this period in
her life may suggest emotions that she could express only
obliquely. At a time when it was not only shameful but
impractical for a woman to retreat from a marriage, many
women transferred their baffled affections to pride in the
status that was theirs because of their husband's accomplishments, allowing their tenderness for the man himself
to fade as devotion to his image increased. However
presumptuous it may be to suspect such a process in
Emilie Reed, it would perhaps offer an explanation for
her puzzling behavior at the end, when she declined to go
to the bedside of her dying husband but held stoutly to her
own reflected importance as his wife, and then widow.
Reed's copious and almost embarrassingly sentimental
letters to her over the years should, perhaps, be taken at
face value; but at times they seem more to suggest patience, devotion to duty, and forbearance than they do
spontaneous communion with someone understood and
understanding at the level of an abiding love.

Here is the story she told.

In the depths of winter when a blizzard had been raging
and the temperature was below zero . . . A man came from
twelve miles in the country for him [Reed] to go to his sick
wife. He started at sunset in a driving wind, there were no
landmarks, only this vast plain of snow . . . so no wonder
that he became lost and on his faithful horse wandered
aimlessly about till midnight, when suddenly from behind
a snowdrift a little beacon of light appeared and he found
the little hut. The woman was quite ill and he did not leave
her bedside till late the next afternoon. Again he was lost,
and did not reach his own fireside till nearly eleven . . . yet

The Plateau

after the welcome home his face brightened and he broke out into a merry laugh as he recalled . . . [that] the old man [had] drawled out, "Well, Doc, I often feels sorry for you folks at the Post, I know you gits lonely." . . . Dr. Reed was at the same time inwardly commiserating the utter loneliness of this poor man and woman in their remote desolation. In starting out on such trips his wife would plead with him not to venture, that his life was too valuable for such hazards. It was only under these circumstances that he would not yield to her persuasions.

As the only physician for hundreds of miles around Fort Robinson, Reed had many nonmilitary patients, but the story of one military case—that he lost—is perpetuated by a specimen in the Army Medical Museum, a bullet removed from the chest of a private hit accidentally when it ricocheted. The annual report of the surgeon general for that year indicates that Reed gave a good account of himself in attempting the necessary thoracic surgery, but was defeated by a collapse of the lung, and surgical shock.

In the spring and summer of 1885, routine medical service took up much of Reed's time, and he was engaged in the usual vexing problems with post administration. The hospital cook was being kept so late at rifle practice that Reed's patients failed to get their evening meal on time, and it took paperwork and pressure to get this straightened out. The place assigned for autopsies was inconveniently and—in view of the danger of infection —dangerously situated, and he succeeded in having it moved. Best of all, he was able in July 1885 to move patients into the new hospital, where they had a proper roof over their heads instead of canvas.

In September his family, including Indian Susie, left for Norfolk, Virginia; since he had no replacement, he was unable to accompany them. The leave he had requested was not granted until December, when he too took off for Norfolk. In January he took a little trip to Florida alone, just in time to see a citrus grove he had optimistically and foolishly purchased some time earlier receive severe damage from frost. February saw him back at Fort Robinson without the family, his hands full of very sick patients.

WALTER REED

The spring of 1887 found him still wrestling with many of the same old problems that had beset him since his arrival three years earlier. There was much sickness still, and it was coming to be realized that the neglect of sanitary engineering could wipe out an entire community. Reed kept making official recommendations for improving the deplorable conditions of drainage and elementary neglect of sanitary precautions—and sometimes they were heeded. After treating innumerable injuries due to the rough life, and dealing with frostbite and respiratory ills that invariably attended the rigorous winters of the region, he was glad that July of 1887 saw him headed for an assignment in the Deep South.

If he had thought to be free of "the Indian problem" by quitting Nebraska for Mount Vernon Barracks, Alabama, he was wrong. In the recently consummated agreement with the Apaches, they had been told that they would be dispersed to live out their lives in the Arizona mountains, but the government sent many of them instead to the warm, damp south, where they fell prey to the white man's plagues. These prisoners were a constant source of embarrassment to the army. General Crook was outraged, especially at the treatment of those among them who had been faithful scouts. Although the Mt. Vernon Barracks hospital was adequate for the care of the military, it could do little for Apaches suffering from tuberculosis, syphilis, malnutrition, alcoholism—and a numbing homesickness for the mountains from which they had been spirited away.

Although Reed was able, for a change, to regard the general sanitary conditions of the post as "excellent," he was concerned about 346 Indians camped outside its walls, suffering from much pulmonary and bronchial disease. And as might be expected, the Indian population had its own miscreants, as was evident when a nine-year-old Indian girl was abducted by an Apache man of bad reputation, who raped and otherwise abused her before a military pursuit of several days brought her back.

As time went on, his concern over tuberculosis among

The Plateau

the captive people became acute. This was a time when pulmonary tuberculosis was rightly feared by all ages and all classes, and it was known that Indians had a particular susceptibility to it, a weakness certainly heightened by the climate into which the government had sent them, so unlike anything to which their race had become biologically adjusted. Reed reported the death of three strong young women who had been well at the time of his earlier report and pointed to the rapidly fatal course the disease was taking among other Indians. He was soon to learn, however, that it was government policy for these redundant people to be annihilated.

There was also scarlet fever among the military to worry about, and much influenza. Insisting prophetically upon screens to keep his patients from the nuisance of mosquitoes and flies, he sought also for an ice machine, citing the baleful effects of letting food spoil in the heat. And he called attention to the need for an engine to step up the flow of water because too little was being delivered to flush the drains.

As is usual, however, even among the caring, private lives continue to run their course when surrounded by trials and the tragedies of others. Emilie Reed wrote of her husband that "After four years in Nebraska he looked upon Alabama, with its balmy sunshine and exquisite flowers as a well chosen spot, and it was there he converted a sandy waste into a most beautiful garden." Young Lawrence Reed, ten years old, was off at the University School in Tuscaloosa, expressing in long letters home his agonies of homesickness and self-doubt among the "old boys." The doctor set out some magnolia trees he had found in the wild; a neighbor begged him to uproot them, claiming that if a transplanted magnolia lived, it would bring the death of a family member within a year. In upholding her husband's scorn of such superstition, Emilie failed to make the connection, in her written account of this, that the family had had word, soon after the transplanting, of the death of Laura Reed Blincoe's husband. His death left Laura penniless with a large brood of children, and although her brother offered his profound sympathy at once, there was very little else he could offer her, a circumstance that distressed him greatly.

By midsummer 1890, Reed's longing for contact with the rapidly progressing world of medicine became acute. This was an era of great excitement and forward leaps in medicine as it became more scientific—and Mount Vernon Barracks was a stagnant backwater. So he asked for a four-month leave "for business purposes . . . and, also, to enable me to avail myself of the opportunity of pursuing certain special studies in my profession."

He was now almost forty, which in 1890, and especially in the army, was considered well past middle age. Cut off from what was happening in the medical centers, ineffectually trying to minister to doomed Indians, responsible for the hygiene of his men but without appropriate resources to insure it, he could look forward to no further training than he could obtain by mail. A splendid all-purpose physician, he could not consider himself an expert in any specialty. He had not been as successful financially as he and his wife had expected, and if he were to be honest with himself he knew that he never would be. His dream of profit from his Florida orange grove had turned into a nightmare, and even more frustrating was his vulnerability to the whim of whoever happened to be his superior by reason of politics or longevity. He was tired of filling out forms in triplicate to add to the red tape of army bureaucracy.

Perhaps it was his restlessness—as well as his perennial need for money—that led him to submit an article on Geronimo for publication in the *Illustrated American*. He had often been called an amusing raconteur, and he could not resist citing the visual benefits offered by the habit generously formed Apache women had of letting their freshly washed clothing dry on their bodies, and noting that virtue among Indian women was well regarded "since the loss of virtue was formerly promptly followed by the loss of the woman's nose."

For a while he despaired about getting the leave he

The Plateau

wanted so badly, for he was told that to do so he must find a replacement and pay him. In August, however, Jedediah Hyde Baxter was made surgeon general, and he was happy to find a medical officer who was eager to learn, so Reed was able to report on October 1, 1890, for a new kind of duty (to the surgeon general of the army in Washington.)

The new surgeon general had long worked for what we would now call continuing education for the army's medical officers. With a degree in law as well as medicine, he had shown great ability as an administrator, and had many far-reaching plans for the improvement of his service. Within four months of his appointment he died of a stroke at the age of fifty-three; but during his brief tenure in office he made some decisions that were momentous for Walter Reed.

The course Reed wanted to take at Johns Hopkins lasted six months, and the leave to which he was entitled when he reported to Baltimore on October 1, 1890, was for only three. The surgeon general's office solved more than one of his problems when it gave him the sinecure (but salaried) job of examining recruits at Fort McHenry in Baltimore, and extended his time so he could be at Hopkins for the seven-months' postgraduate session in pathology and bacteriology.

CHAPTER IV

The Upswing

Walter Reed could not have been more fortunate than to have had his only period of time off for study in the fall of the 1890–91 year, and to spend it in the new Johns Hopkins Hospital, opened during the previous year. (The medical school did not open until 1893, because of financial conditions.) John Shaw Billings had selected William Henry Welch as Dean and Professor of Pathology and had helped get William Osler, William S. Halsted, and Howard Kelly. He also designed the hospital and medical school buildings.

Welch, who had been responsible for setting up the department of pathology, wrote later that although Reed started his work on the clinical side of the hospital, he was soon allowed to "follow his own inclination and to enter the regular courses in pathology and bacteriology in the Pathological Laboratory," where he found in "the new fields of scientific medicine . . . the centre of his professional interest and activity" and something that "he himself was destined to cultivate with such signal benefits to medical science and to the welfare of mankind."

It must be remembered that the latter part of the century was a great period of medical discovery concerned with the infectious diseases. Welch notes that "Upon the basis of the discoveries of Pasteur and Koch, and particularly . . . the new methods introduced by Koch for the cultivation and study of bacteria . . . there had followed in rapid succession . . . such important discoveries as those of the specific germs causing tuberculosis, cholera, leprosy, glanders, erysipelas, surgical infections, tetanus, pneumonia, typhoid fever, malaria, amoebic dysentery, cerebro-spinal meningitis, diphtheria, and a large number of animal diseases." But disease *control*—the ultimate aim of such research—depends on more than identification of the causative agent. It is necessary first to learn how the organism may be overcome in the sufferer's body, so that those already infected may have hope of recovery. Then, some way of conferring immunity must be sought, some way of modifying the organism so that a vaccine may be developed to prevent or ameliorate the disease. And the manner of the organism's transmittal must be definitively established before any effective public health measure against its spread can be put into operation. When one realizes that transmittal of the yellow fever virus depends on an intermediate host (vector) of one sex in one subspecies of insect, and upon not only the length of time since it invaded the body of the prime sufferer but also how long it has been in the vector, one rejoices that Walter Reed was introduced to bacteriology by some of the keenest research people of the time.

He flowered during his time at Hopkins. Welch noted that "After he had acquired familiarity with technical methods he undertook advanced and independent work. He attended post-mortem examinations and sometimes conducted them, and was accustomed to study for himself pathological material and cultures—obtained from autopsies." He ran a series of experiments clarifying a problem in the pathology of typhoid fever; and one can see a hint of destiny in his work with Dr. Welch on the identification of the hog cholera bacillus; without this experience he could not have stood his ground so firmly later when Sanarelli, his bitter opponent in yellow fever research, accused him of confusing the hog cholera bacillus with "his" organism that caused yellow fever. In spite of his independent work and his absorption in the new field opening out before him, he had time to enjoy real fellowship with his distinguished associates. These included, besides the Great Four, Henry Hurd and Simon Flexner, who was to discover *Shigella dysenteriae* in the Philippines in 1912, and whose brother was to publish in 1910 his great challenge to medical education. They all seem to have responded as readily to Reed's genial personality as to his professional zeal.

But he was still in the uniform of his country, and just before Christmas he was ordered to Fort Keogh, Montana. The Sioux, in what now seems an infinitely pathetic hope, were clinging to the belief that a millennium was at hand, and that the return of ghosts from their past would enable them to annihilate the white man and recover the lands of their forefathers. Sitting Bull had been killed (under suspicious circumstances) on December 19, some three weeks before Reed arrived to care for the victims of this saddest of all army confrontations. The old Sioux had led his people at Little Big Horn—and had, incidentally, protested the sale of 11,000,000 acres of Sioux land at fifty cents an acre. Washington had decided that "the savages" were an unwarranted nuisance, and the Seventh Cavalry was, in any case, eager to avenge Custer. The bloodshed at what came to be known as the Battle of Wounded Knee was terrible. Many of the victims were Indian women cut down as they fled with babies in their arms. One historian, Herbert Welsh, has said that the battle, which occurred on December 20, looked "as though blind rage had been at work." Between 300 and 400 "savages" were murdered. The memory of that day still inflames Indians living in that region.

Reed's duties toward the wounded Americans included

excision of the fragments of a watch driven into the abdominal wall of one Lieutenant Hawthorne, who was lucky enough to have the bullet that hit him buffered by his timepiece. A meticulous description of the removal of mainspring, ratchet wheels, glass, and watch case remains lost in the army records. By mid-January the Sioux surrendered en masse, bringing to an end the last of the Indian Wars, and Reed was soon reunited with his family at their rented home at 1122 Madison Avenue, near the Hopkins Hospital.

Although at his wife's insistence Reed bought twelve acres in Blue Ridge Summit, an ideal retreat from the blazing summer heat of Washington and Baltimore, he had known all along that the Hopkins experience was too good to last, and he began worrying about his next assignment. Meanwhile—and over the years that followed —the family took great pleasure in their country place, which they named Keewaydin, using the Indian term for "west wind." Whenever he could, the doctor became a gardener. He had a splendid green thumb, as well as a joyous affinity with the land inculcated during his boyhood.

When he approached the influential John Shaw Billings —then curator of the Army Museum and librarian of the Surgeon General's Library in Washington—for help in obtaining a post in the capital city, he received little encouragement. He was, in fact, sent for a month's service on an army examining board in New York City, and then had to face the bitter disappointment of being assigned to Fort Snelling, Minnesota. He fully expected to remain there for the usual two- to four-year tour of duty before going to another wilderness outpost, and had his household effects, which he had left in Mount Vernon Barracks, sent on. He assumed his new duty on November 7, 1891.

Shortly thereafter he was made an honorary member of the Ramsey County Medical Society—the first medical society he had been invited to join since his stay in New York. Reed was asked to address the society on the subject of Asiatic cholera. An epidemic of cholera had broken out

The Upswing

in Hamburg, Germany, and there was worldwide fear of a pandemic. It was thought that the United States might be vulnerable to the kind of wildfire epidemic that had raged in Europe during the nineteenth century. Reed's lecture compared the work of Koch and the German commission with that of the French commission. The lecture gave him an opportunity to meet Louis Wilson, who was to become the director of the Mayo Foundation, but who, at the time of their meeting, was teaching biology in St. Paul's Central High School. Wilson was introduced to the speaker as "a man who had a laboratory."

But Walter Reed was never allowed to become smug. His new commanding officer gave him a fitness report so indifferent as to be, under the circumstances, insulting. His chief stated that the new doctor had no special scientific attainments to offer, no outstanding characteristics or special aptitude, and had demonstrated no desire to go beyond the daily routine of duty. This report tells less about its subject than it does about the disdain felt for medical officers in the army. A medical officer could expect indifference from a line officer, and might face real hostility, although by the 1890s there was a glimmer of recognition that the public health function of the medics might be useful. Colonel Mason may have been only a little old-fashioned in failing to recognize the contribution of the medics, which was soon to be so dramatically highlighted in the Spanish-American War, but his slight came at a bad time for a man hungry for encouragement that one day his circumstances and his stature might improve.

It hurt Reed to have to write to his sister Laura, who was always in need of financial help, that he could offer very little. He had lost $3,500 in his ill-fated investment in a Florida orange grove. His wife was asserting herself, no doubt reminding him that charity begins at home. He wrote of his monthly payment of $60 for the place at Blue Ridge Summit, and, noting that he must make like payments until July 1894, declared that he felt "almost like giving up the ghost," and ventured sadly that he would "have to *desert* and ship off to the South Sea Islands!" He

WALTER REED

spoke of household expenses, the cost of life insurance, and the amount it took to keep Lawrence in school.

He was thinking of sending Lawrence to another school, having become greatly upset over a Methodist revival of the fire-and-brimstone variety held at Randolph-Macon Academy. It had, he said, greatly troubled his "loving, truthful, charitable and tenderhearted boy" with convictions of sin. He wrote such heated objections to the school's administration that one is obliged to wonder if he did not sometimes unconsciously connect his disappointments in life with the absence of worldly advantages in a childhood home dominated by evangelistic fervor. He always remained conventionally devoted to his parson father, whom he describes as a "dear old gentleman" with an "exquisite appetite" and "wonderful vitality for a man of his years," and uttered the wish that he himself "could lead such a useful life." But it could not have escaped him that although his brother Kit had become a judge of the Kansas Supreme Court in 1887, and Jim was a well-established Methodist minister, the parson's other children continued to struggle for an existence. He wrote to Laura, that docile, hard-pressed daughter: "I am willing to agree with you that our dear father is in many respects a remarkable man, and, in all respects a pure and true man, but I think that his eldest Daughter is really a *more remarkable MAN* than he is! . . . He is the Salt of the Earth, and you, my dear sister, are the Salter!"

Anyone who interprets this brotherly regard as evidence that Reed believed in the equality of women should be warned that in another letter he took great pains to caution Laura against allowing her daughter to put any undue energy into her studies at a time when her body was undergoing the biological stresses of female development. This avuncular medical advice apparently fell on deaf ears, however, for one of Laura's daughters took off at an early age to teach school in Old Mexico, no place at that time for a young gringa who was not shrewdly resourceful. The circumstances of her going are unclear, but her uncle exchanged letters with her, practicing (rath-

The Upswing

er clumsily) the Spanish he had, providentially, begun to learn in Arizona in the 1870s.

In the spring of 1892 Reed was assigned to stand by with medical care when the land rush in the vicinity of the Wahpeton-Sisseton Reservation took place. A presidential proclamation made land available on April 15 on a first-come, first-served basis. It was thought necessary to assign the army to maintain some kind of order in the rush of land seekers to stake their claims in the 600,000 fertile acres. But in spite of an enormous crowd, the event, though colorful in the extreme, was relatively peaceful, and the army was soon sent back, ambulances and all. In August Reed was transferred to the city of St. Paul. Since he was to care for the government's civilian employees rather than for soldiers, the family lived in quite a grand hotel, one then called the Albion. But the budget allowed no leeway for self-indulgence. Reed wrote his sister that his salary was $252.67 a month, and that expenses were $251, leaving him only "the snug little sum of $1.67 on which to 'cavort.'" He was paying $65 a month for rent, $100 for board, and $10 for laundry. A cleaning woman got $2.50 a month, Blossom's music teacher, $5.00. Piano rental amounted to $6. He was able to save $3.00 a month by walking instead of taking the streetcar. "St. Paul is an expensive town, . . ." he wrote, "But never mind if I can only get through '93 and '94 safely, my head should once more be well out of water. '93 will be my hardest year, as I expect my next promotion in '94, when my salary will be increased $50.00 per month."

Reed and Louis Wilson worked together improvising in the high school laboratory "fairly effective bacteriological apparatus—mostly from gas ovens and boilers inherited from a discontinued Domestic Science Department!" They secured from Dr. William Park of the New York City Laboratory a "sample box, holding two test tubes, one containing a sterile swab and the other a solidified serum culture medium." Their purpose was to follow Park in making the diagnosis of diphtheria "from cultures made from the swabs of patients' throats," and they used some of their own money to have a local box factory make 100 similar boxes. These they distributed to several St. Paul physicians with the request that they take swabs from the throats of suspected diphtheria cases, and forward them to the two investigators. Wilson noted, "I think this was the first attempt at the examination of throat cultures for Bacillus diphtheriae west of New York." Dr. Reed was beginning to practice his new specialty.

CHAPTER V

Washington

The selection of George Miller Sternberg as surgeon general in May 1893 was to have a profound effect on the life of Walter Reed. Sternberg was a scientist, not an army politician, and at the time of his selection, he was a bacteriologist of impeccable reputation and an internationally recognized authority on yellow fever. Until their beliefs about the cause of the disease came into collision some years later, the two men enjoyed a most cordial relationship marked by mutual respect. Reed wrote a letter of congratulation when he heard of the appointment, saying "it places at the head of the Corps the one man who preeminently stands forth as the representative of progressive scientific medicine. . . . The fossil age has passed."

The new Surgeon General's first move was the establishment of the Army Medical School, in spite of the parsimonious mood of Congress caused by the panic of 1893. Ignoring the faltering economy, Sternberg set up his school almost surreptitiously. Rather than demanding funds, he simply used as faculty those army officers who had appropriate training and talent and who, after being assigned to Washington on army duty, could teach in addition to doing whatever else was expected of them. For laboratories and classrooms he used rooms in the old Army Medical Museum on Seventh and B streets S.W. In June the school was chartered "for the purpose of instructing approved candidates for admission to the Medical Corps of the Army in their duties as medical officers."

It was to open in November, and to require four months of instruction. "Four professors will be selected from among the senior medical officers of the Army stationed in or near the city of Washington, and as many associate professors as may be required to give practical laboratory instruction in the methods of sanitary analysis, microscopical technique, clinical microscopy, bacteriology, urine analysis, &c." The faculty would deliver lectures on the duties of medical officers in war and peace. A professor of military surgery would touch on the care and transportation of the wounded. A professor of military hygiene would give "practical instruction in the examination of air, water, food, and clothing from a sanitary point of view." As "Professor of Clinical and Sanitary Microscopy," Reed would include elements of bacteriology and urinology in his instruction.

In December a newly promoted Major Reed found a place in this new school and was made curator of the Army Medical Museum as well. Sternberg had been much impressed with Reed's work at Hopkins with Welch and others in 1890, and saw in him more than a careful frontier medic. Reed had indeed become an expert military epidemiologist. After so many disappointments, he found himself at last in an enormously congenial post that was gratifying to both his family and himself, and with resources at his command. He now bore the titles of professor of clinical and sanitary microscopy and curator of the Army Medical Museum. He was at last joyously in the middle of things that mattered to him and no longer a sort of supernumerary surgeon to be sent to one remote and uncomfortable outpost after another!

As curator of the Army Medical Museum, he followed John Shaw Billings, who had been appointed to that post in 1883. Museums were still important in teaching; the museum's specimens, some from the Civil War and the Indian wars in the West, provided teaching material. Reed was stepping into big shoes; Billings, who had been influential in the establishment of the Johns Hopkins Hospital and the staffing of its medical school, was a brilliant man of great accomplishments. Said to have been "an intellectual aristocrat," he was far less interested in the science of medicine than in the organization of medical knowledge. He originated Index Medicus and other library systems and developed the science of biostatistics in this country. Clearly, Reed's new superiors did not concur with Colonel Mason's view that he "had no special scientific attainments to offer, and no special aptitude."

Others of Reed's new associates were interesting men. Charles Smart, a Scot, had taken advantage of his experiences as a soldier in the Wild West to write a novel about it. A chemist, he had made an abortive effort under the National Board of Health to test foodstuffs for adulterants; the fact that political pressures put a stop to this endeavor did nothing to stop his ultimate advance to the rank of brigadier general. George Martin Kober, a German immigrant who had risen from the ranks of the army to take medicine at Columbia University, had become an anthropologist of note and later was the recipient of honors for his work in housing and in tuberculosis control. In the last year of Reed's life, Kober rented their family an apartment in the house he owned at 1603 Nineteenth Street Northwest.

And what was most important, Baltimore was near enough to Washington to permit the renewal of friendships begun at Hopkins during his earlier stay in the east. One of these Hopkins acquaintances was to stand at his side in some of the most critical moments of his life, but was to leave a resentful footnote to his yellow fever research. This was James Carroll, who, according to Dr. Welch, had, as a hospital steward at Hopkins, helped Reed in the laboratories, showing a "peculiar aptitude" for the work. An English workingman who, by his own account, had just "drifted into the Army" after being a blacksmith's helper, a railroad laborer, and a lumberjack, Carroll had asked to be allowed to attend medical lectures. Refused at first, he was able later to attend lectures at the University of the City of New York and at the University of Maryland, where he got his medical degree in 1891. He did postgraduate work at Hopkins, and perhaps this association led to Reed's sending for him to help in Washington. Welch notes that the two men "frequently came back here together to attend lectures two or three times a week, and kept fully in touch with the research work going on in the laboratories." For some time the Reed-Carroll team was warm and effective. Outranked and outclassed, Carroll felt honored at first by having been chosen to assist Reed, but the erstwhile hospital steward was rather pathetically unable to deal with his envy and hurt self-esteem toward the end of their association and after Reed died.

The Reeds lived in Georgetown, in the 3000 block of Q Street. Georgetown then was not quite the chic place it is today, but it was quietly respectable. Lawrence went to high school in Washington. Blossom could play outside in safety and run to meet her father in the evening when he got off the streetcar. The elder Reeds took advantage of the theater and enjoyed a simple social life with friends, mostly military officers and their wives. Neither his background nor his character disposed Walter Reed to engage in the social game for advantage. It was enough to have the wandering family settled comfortably at last, and to be where events were taking shape, instead of waiting in some remote spot for stale news of the world. The capital city was growing, making great efforts to become a cultural as well as a governmental center. And it did not take long to get to work on the trolley; the trip gave him time to think, anyway.

He was forty-two when he became a professor, and had

Washington

previously had no formal teaching experience. He was beginning to know for the first time the stimulation and excitement of kindling the minds of other men. It was a challenge to explore a complicated new subject, but it was equally a challenge to keep the attention of physicians— some of whom were present because of the army's orders rather than through any interest of their own. The twenty-odd students enrolled in the first session, which ran from October 1893 to March 1894, had all passed stiff entrance examinations, but their background training ranged from questionable to excellent. There were many problems in presenting a field as newly developed as bacteriology, with its unfamiliar terms and unstandardized nomenclature and its unique demands for precision in laboratory technique. Although the new teacher wrote to his sister that "My duties are new to me and hence my work is just twenty times as hard as it ought to be," he became an excellent teacher, expressing himself in the same amazingly concise and logical way with which he produced papers, designed research, and carried out a myriad of other duties under pressure. One of his students wrote:

> His lectures, beside satisfying the zealous seeker for knowledge, were spiced with humor, . . . which made the relations between him and his students a freer and more sympathetic one. His language was always interesting. . . . When he was at his best, his voice would reach a high falsetto note . . . due to his characteristic method of impressing important facts upon dull or indurate intellects. His students never feared him, but from the start regarded him with filial affection. . . . He was constantly at the side of his pupils in the laboratory, advising, encouraging, counselling, and, above all, instructing.

The students spent the first two weeks learning a few principles of laboratory technique with nonpathogenic organisms and then started right in with the pathogenic ones. They learned about autopsies, animal experiments, demonstrations, and the recovery of organisms in pure culture. Such phenomena as inflammation were studied in vivo. The time was one of tremendous scientific advance:

WALTER REED

Von Ermengen identified the organism of botulism; Yersin and Kitasato, those of plague. An antitoxin was discovered for diphtheria as a result of the research of von Behring and Emile Roux. But the American public, including the doctors, was not impressed. The times were hard. Three million people were out of work, and there were no programs in those days to provide medical care for the poor or food for the hungry.

In March, Reed was made a member of the Medical Society of the District of Columbia. Diphtheria was discussed at the first meeting he attended as a member, and he contributed his views on the nature and spread of this disease at some length, stressing the importance to diagnosis of the often neglected bacteriological examination. The May meeting was devoted to a discussion of tuberculosis, to which Reed contributed his negative opinion concerning the possibility that a mother recently vaccinated against smallpox might transmit tuberculosis to the infant she was carrying because lymph from a tuberculous cow, used in the vaccine, might contain tubercle bacilli. He did note that the disease could be transmitted in utero by a tuberculous mother, that this was most likely in the latter months of a pregnancy, and that the highest mortality from the disease occurred in the first and second years of life. Tuberculosis became more than a professional concern to him in June, when, on a visit to his sister, he recognized that she had the disease. His advice was to "nail the windows open and take the doors off the hinges." This trust in fresh air was not in accord with the beliefs of the day, but Laura Blincoe did recover. It is hard to grasp the fear of tuberculosis that prevailed then, in a day when one writer claimed that throughout the world 5,000,000 die annually because of it and one American city's newspaper credited it with killing 12 percent of the population.

The first meeting of the Medical Society in January 1895 returned to a consideration of diphtheria. Almost unknown today, this disease was, quite properly, greatly feared as a sudden killer of young children. The Pasteur Institute began producing antitoxin after the great excitement occasioned by reports of its efficacy in September 1894 at the Eighth International Congress of Hygiene and Demography at Budapest. It was used for the first time in the United States on two patients in the Willard Parker Hotel in New York on New Year's Day 1895. Three months later, results of its use were less exciting than had been expected; fatality had been reduced to only 27 percent from the former rate of 32 percent. Theobald Smith was to work for nine years under the auspices of Harvard to produce and distribute increasing amounts of antitoxin of ever increasing potency.

The concept of toxin and antitoxin was a difficult one. Joseph Kinyoun of the U.S. Marine Hospital Service reported that "While the serum would not work miracles, yet its effects were little short of marvelous. In cases of plain diphtheria, where the patient could be seen early in the disease, the mortality was practically nothing. But even in cases where there were complications the mortality was reduced to less than one half." He emphasized that "antitoxin is not only a cure for the disease—it is also a preventive."

According to the society's minutes, Walter Reed took issue with what he considered Dr. Kinyoun's oversimplification. Although he himself had not treated diphtheria with antitoxin, he had been sent 10 cc of Aronson's serum in October and had injected it into two guinea pigs and two rabbits. Always practical, he stressed that a physician oriented to the laboratory might find it fairly easy to diagnose diphtheria, but that a practicing clinician might find it difficult to make cultures; and that the application of an antiseptic before taking the culture would compromise any diagnosis in which the culture was a determinant. He pointed out incidentally—and prophetically—how tempting to unscrupulous entrepreneurs the manufacture and control of effective drugs might become.

A report from Walter Reed, Sanitary Inspector, which appeared in the *Journal of the American Medical Association* that January, indicates the doctor was vigilant on more than one front. Those living in Washington today and

accustomed to the malodorous Potomac will find it interesting that when Reed subjected a specimen of Potomac
River ice to bacteriologic examination, the result was "that
with five plates made, each with one cubic centimeter of
water, only a few colonies of the bacillus convolutus, a
common water organism, were found." To the investiga-
tor's surprise, it contained "fewer colonies of bacteria than
any of the other specimens of ice so far examined by us in
the laboratory."

Rabies was interesting to the members of the medical
society, and the new member had something to say about
this also. He had recently identified the disease in specimens from a dog that had bitten one woman who had survived after receiving the Pasteur treatment, and another
who had died without it. He gave an admirable account of
rabies, as it was then understood; up-to-date knowledge
would add little save the elaboration on diagnosing on the
basis of brain specimens from rabid animals. Characteristi-
cally, he cited explicit references that would enable anyone
interested to pursue the matter further. After giving data
on the reduction of rabies cases in the large cities of
Europe after the adoption of a tax on dogs, he gave a
description that is classic of a rabid dog. He noted that
although people thought that an infected animal would
become fierce right away, it would be very quiet for some
time, lying in a secluded place until it became restless. It
would still obey commands, but slowly. Then it would
hallucinate and bite at imaginary objects. It would eat
ravenously, not showing until later the fear of water that
gives the disease its other name, hydrophobia.

His work on rabies was good preparation for what was
to come. He had become aware of the world of rapidly
multiplying organisms that were hard or impossible to
isolate. Pasteur had shown that the causative agent of a
disease did not have to be identified before it could be
attacked, and rabies was partly mastered by a treatment
that vanquished a still invisible enemy. Reed collaborated
with Sternberg on a paper published in *Transactions of the
Association of American Physicians*, entitled "Report on Im-

munity against Vaccination Conferred upon the Monkey by the Use of the Serum, and the Vaccinated Calf and Monkey." This is interesting because of Sternberg's explanation that there might be an antitoxin in the serum of immunized calves that could give immunity to smallpox. It is perhaps more interesting, however, because it indicates that in their experiments Sternberg and Reed used human subjects—"unvaccinated children in some of the orphan asylums in the city of Brooklyn." No one was squeamish then about using such hopelessly situated children in experiments that might indeed save their own lives as well as the lives of others.

Saying that important official duties kept him from continuing this research, Sternberg suggested that Walter Reed take over. Reed took serum from the blood of a successfully vaccinated calf to see if it would have any effect on smallpox, ". . . to ascertain what effect the serum would manifest in conferring immunity against vacinia in the monkey especially as Copeman had recently pointed out that this animal rhoesus [*sic*] was quite susceptible to vaccination." After reporting on the inconclusive studies of Raynaud, Reed discussed Sternberg's earlier work and some other studies. Since their results were negative, Sternberg's notion that serum of a vaccinated calf might contain some antitoxic substance was not verified. Sternberg defended the use of antitoxin in diphtheria, although by this time the disastrous failure of Koch's tuberculin as a cure for tuberculosis had raised questions in the public mind about the efficacy of new medical discoveries.

Even in 1895 the medical establishment had public relations problems. An attack on "Sundown Doctors and Evening Colleges" came from within the establishment itself—in the January issue of the *Journal of the American Medical Association*, which spoke scornfully of "a number of graduated physicians who attend patients after office hours," and sniffed at Washington's night schools. It is hard to understand today why evening classes were such anathema, and it was common practice for army medical officers in Washington to have a consulting medical practice. Maj. William Borden, a friend of Reed's, was, for example, much sought after by private surgical patients. The Surgeon General's Office had no official prejudice against its medics practicing in off-duty hours, and many of its staff members served on the faculty of the Columbian University Medical School. Low army pay and the high cost of living in the capital made extra earnings most attractive. It was a great help to Walter Reed's financial prospects when he was invited in June to join this faculty himself.

As professor of pathology and bacteriology he taught a course consisting of didactic lectures and laboratory instruction in pathology, pathological histology, and bacteriology. The sum of six hundred dollars was borrowed from the university for the equipment of a laboratory, and James Carroll and William Washburn were appointed to assist Reed, who was paid $500 a session. Since this academic appointment was followed by his being made a delegate to the American Public Health Association, his standing in the medical community as well as his financial situation improved that month.

Before assuming his new duties at the medical school, Reed had a welcome respite at Keewaydin with his family. He reported to Laura that although he had been losing weight in Washington, he had been so greatly renewed at Keewaydin that he had "gained 20 pounds and come back feeling as gay as a goat." "I am a 'way back' farmer," he added. "Inherit it from my father." The excessive heat made it wise for him to leave his family at Blue Ridge Summit and return to Washington alone, but it was satisfying to know that they could be comfortable.

In the hot fall of 1895 he began his first epidemiological work, a study of an outbreak of malaria at Washington Barracks and at Fort Myer, across the Potomac. What was then known about malaria was well summarized in Osler's famous textbook, *Principles and Practices of Medicine*, first published in 1892. The natural history of the disease was well known, and its curious periodicities and its affinity for some places, particularly hot and swampy places, was recognized. A Frenchman named Lavaran, working in North Africa, had described the responsible parasite as early as 1880, attracting no attention in his homeland. Patrick Manson—as yet an unknown scientist working in the Orient, far from the academic or journalistic arena of science—had found a clue in the transmitting of filariae responsible for elephantiasis by mosquitoes, but he thought that the disease occurred when an infected mosquito died and contaminated drinking water. Ross, writing in 1894 in the *Indian Medical Gazette* of his discovery of the life history of the malarial parasite, with the mosquito as intermediary host, gave credit to Manson, who subsequently won a Nobel Prize for this important clue and founded the London School of Tropical Medicine. But Reed, though entirely familiar with malaria, had not been impressed by any relationship between the appearance of malaria in any one place and the prevalence of mosquitoes there. Thus, in Washington, he had opposed the suggestion made by Alfred Freeman Africanus King that the mosquitoes might be the vector. King's paper included so many obvious inaccuracies that his colleagues wrote the whole thing off, thus rejecting a supposition that was in fact as accurate as it was rash. So when Reed began his work on malaria, the night air from the swamps may have been suspect, but the insects with a deadly cargo borne on that same swamp breeze were overlooked.

Reed's reports on this study were buried for years in the official archives. They begin with the ingenuous but apparently entirely acceptable explanation that although Reed received his orders on August 30, his annual leave at Blue Ridge Summit was to begin on that very day, so he could not start the project until the first week in October. The study lasted, then, from the first week in October to mid-November. The late fall was, as it happened, as lucky for the researchers as it was unlucky for the soldiers, since there was no frost to kill the mosquitoes that kept the epidemics going at the two military posts, and there was much clinical material. His report discarded the notion that malaria is waterborne, received in drinking water.

After all, like the sick soldiers, fever-free Washington also used Potomac water, and in 1895, when carefully filtered Potomac water instead of water from springs and wells was used at Fort Myer, there was more malaria than in any of the preceding twenty-three years.

Reed compared the year's experience with that of former years; the army garrison's experience with that of the city of Washington; the region's experience with that of any other with acceptable epidemiological records. He checked meteorological variations from year to year. He took into account all the variables connected with whether or not a camp had a full complement, and the origin of that complement. He found that people living near the river in Washington had a higher death rate than those elsewhere in the city; that although 240 feet higher than and half a mile inland from the Potomac, Fort Myer had a high rate—and an even higher one after the water was sanitized; that black soldiers, often exposed to the worst conditions, had less malaria than the white; and that tertian malaria predominated at Fort Myer, but estivoautumnal, at Washington Barracks. The marshlands certainly seemed to be the source of trouble. And quinine continued to be a good remedy.

In spite of this exhaustive—and exhausting—but inconclusive study, Reed found the time and energy to reenter the argument about the effectiveness of diphtheria antitoxin at a December meeting of the medical society. Anyone acquainted with the history of science knows that new discoveries designed to help mankind often awaken public suspicion and arouse the skepticism of the discoverer's peers and even their hatred rather than their enthusiasm and gratitude. Although this situation may in some cases simply indicate appropriate caution as well as man's built-in suspicion of the new, one cannot overlook the possibility that it makes for furious combat among those who feel envious in assessing the new benefit. This hostile reaction, inescapably central in the story of Walter Reed, had perhaps special justification in the case of the diphtheria antitoxin, however, since early results were erratic.

Washington

Reed backed his belief in the curative efficacy of the antitoxin by statistics from London, Paris, and Berlin, where mortality from the disease had been considerably reduced by its use. And, like any good lecturer, he used anecdote, telling of a patient who had been treated at Washington Barracks for follicular tonsillitis, whose culture, taken at Reed's suggestion, showed the Klebs-Löffler diptheria bacillus. The medical officer would not agree with Reed that the bacillus indicated diphtheria in the absence of characteristic clinical symptoms, and refused to use antitoxin. Five days later, however, he rushed into Reed's laboratory in great excitement, announcing that his patient had suddenly developed laryngeal diphtheria and would surely die without antitoxin. The antitoxin was given, and the patient recovered.

Attributing some of the hostility toward the antitoxin to disappointment with the Koch tuberculin, he pointed out that the two materials were fundamentally different. "The one is toxine, the other antitoxin. The [tuberculin] . . . destroys tuberculous tissue wherever found in the body. . . . The other does not destroy a cell, living or dead. . . . The first agent is manufactured in the human laboratory; the second agent in nature's laboratory, the animal body: so that whatever unfavorable conclusions have been formed in your minds concerning tuberculin, they should have no bearing whatever in the . . . acceptance or rejection of antitoxic serum." He went on to report the tragic increase in deaths among children in one clinic when the supply of antitoxin gave out, concluding that "the failure to use it in a case of human diphtheria is criminal . . . do not, through any fear of its peculiar action, withhold this invaluable remedy!"

An entertaining interruption to the preoccupation with all of these grim concerns was provided by the closing ceremonies of the 1895–96 session of the Army Medical School, which was attended as a gala by many prominent Washingtonians and was addressed by the distinguished J. H. Brinton of Philadelphia, one of the founders of the museum. Brinton noted that it had not been easy to "popularize . . . the surrender to the Surgeon-General's Office of human specimens." He recalled that after "medical officers in field and hospital felt that the Medical Department was really in earnest," it was possible to send collectors to the front to secure specimens "accruing after action on the field." These specimens, "the aggregate of the operating tables," were "roughly cleaned . . . packed in barrels and forwarded to Washington." He noted that in 1862 the museum had had only "three dried and varnished specimens" and identified specimen no. 1335 as the cause of considerable controversy. It came "from a leg crushed by a twelve-pound shot at Gettysburg," and had been forwarded to the museum in a makeshift coffin on which a visiting card read "With the compliments of Major General D.E.S., U.S. Volunteers." The original owner of the limb, a man from the ranks, demanded its return, only to be told that it would not be surrendered. "But it's mine!" he insisted, "Part of myself!" A quick-witted young assistant asked the claimant the length of his enlistment obligation. When the man replied that he had signed up "for three years or the war," the assistant pointed out that his contract had not yet terminated. "Come back at the end of the war," he assured the soldier, "and you can have your bone. In the meantime one detachment of you is stationed in this Museum on government duty, the other wherever you may be ordered. Such," he added brashly, "is the opinion of the Attorney General."

CHAPTER VI

Some Medical Advances— and a War

Oddly enough, at a time when the use of orphan children in medical experimentation raised no public outcry, antivivisectionists were sufficiently well organized to promote a Senate bill forbidding animal experimentation and to attack the Army Medical Museum for its practices. Sternberg and Reed felt obliged to protest to the commissioners of the District in January. But this emotionally charged issue is seldom laid to rest for long, and in the spring a Dr. Rauterberg wrote the Senate committee that he had once been engaged in the "Microscopical Division" of the museum and had then witnessed the "most inhumane and barbarous mutilations of the dumb animal, under the supervision and with the sanction of the . . . officers in charge." He reported that an organ would be removed without anesthesia, and the animal caged to await another mutilation. He claimed to have seen "animals with eyes, section of brain and other parts removed, and kept in reserve for future experiments for a number of days, and

all for the verification and repetition of results obtained
and published years ago." Reed knew such accusations to
be false and was able to obtain from Dr. McConnell,
recently retired from the museum, a statement that "at no
time during my connection with the . . . Museum, from
about 1870 to . . . 1895, have any experiments been per-
formed upon animals in which an anaesthetic was not
used, unless some of the ordinary inoculation experiments, which are practically painless, nor were animals
kept in a mutilated condition." In view of this statement,
the Senate asked that societies and colleges in the District
form a Joint Commission on Vivisection, and Reed was
appointed a member.

The medical society continued its discussion of malaria,
and Reed continued to participate. One of the issues that
raised questions was the confusion of the appearance
under the microscope of parasites and the pigment of
degenerate blood cells. Reed claimed that "there was no
more resemblance between the nucleus of a leucocyte and
a malarial parasite than . . . between the Dome of the
Capitol and the Washington Monument!" Another issue
concerned claims that something called "typho-malaria"
existed. He maintained that "in regard to the complication
of typhoid fever with malarial infection, producing the
so-called typho-malarial fever, it was a very rare occur-
rence," admitting that he had heard of eleven cases, but
insisting that "Where the microscope was used typho-
malarial fever was eliminated."

It was on All Fool's Day that he undertook to refute the
statement of the persistent Dr. A. F. A. King that "you
could have mosquitoes without malaria . . . but you did
not have malaria without . . . mosquitoes." He could readily understand, he said, "that the mosquito biting a patient
with malarial fever might carry away the malarial parasite,
and surely the mosquito could deposit this organism in the
marshes," but he could not believe that it could then bring
it back and inoculate anyone with it. He scoffed at the
picture of a mosquito's engulfing the large amount of
blood he thought necessary for the transmission of ma-

laria, and pointed out his belief that since the mosquito's meal runs uptube, the plasmodium would have to flow in the wrong direction to be injected with a bite. It was to be May 1901 before he would acknowledge his error before another meeting of the society—the one at which he presented his own findings about yellow fever.

In midsummer of 1896 he was sent to Florida to study a smallpox epidemic in Key West. The mission misfired, since the epidemic was short-lived and produced little clinical material. The trip was memorable, however, for his gaining the friendship of his host, Jefferson Randolph Kean, who was to be his dearest friend for the rest of his life and his most impassioned defender. A Virginian of impeccably aristocratic ancestry, Kean had graduated from the University of Virginia's medical school in 1883. When he bade Reed goodbye in Key West on August 4, he sent him off with a gift of mangoes and guava paste and wrote in his diary that Reed was "a charming fellow."

In an almost ecstatic bread-and-butter letter, Reed described his trip to Biscayne Bay as delightful except for "an Army of Mosquitoes" at the last; and a more turbulent passage on another boat up the coast—"tropical and beautiful beyond description." A second letter expressed longing for "that dream life at Key West," and then wistfully assured Kean that if he would only come to Washington, he would be given "the best window, best microscope and best attention." This letter concluded with disgust over William Jennings Bryan's campaign for the presidency.

Reed's retreat to Keewaydin that year was, as usual, the source of great refreshment. He took up bicycling there, and became such an enthusiast that on his return he pedaled blithely along the tree-lined streets of Washington. He wrote Laura in September that he had "been up in the mountains for several weeks, enjoying a much needed rest of mind and body. Was pretty . . . run down and couldn't work with any degree of interest. I have gained 10 lbs. and have the appetite of a 'digger' Indian." But the benefits of his stay at Keewaydin seem to have been

short-lived, for he wrote to his father at the end of the year
that "I never was so busy in my life, & I sometimes get so
weary that I want to lie down and die! Life is not worth
living when the mind is kept on a continual, never-ceasing
strain! I am praying for March to come when my classes
will be over."

Meanwhile, he complained that he was not given
enough time to accomplish all that he wanted to do as a
teacher. "Much to my regret, I was unable to complete the
full and necessary study of the various pathological conditions of the blood." "Coming to this work without previous
experience as a teacher, I am only just learning what the
course in my department should embrace, and I am
convinced that until such time as the medical schools
graduate men who are well grounded in pathological
histology, provision must be made for this instruction in
the Army Medical School." In the spring of 1897 he asked
to resign, saying that his museum duties left him no time
for the medical college, but he was asked to withhold his
resignation.

Medical discoveries—and claims of discoveries—were
coming thick and fast. In February 1897, Dr. Guiseppe
Sanarelli, an Italian working in South America, declared
that "the microbe of yellow fever now splendidly presents
itself, and is the strangest of all microbes that are known."
He was talking about the *Bacillus icteroides*. Novy of Michigan thought Sanarelli's work, which had involved five
human subjects, had been slipshod and inconclusive. This
was, of course, only the opening phase of a long-drawn-
out battle over the causative agent in yellow fever, an
outbreak of which was reported in *Medical News* in September as being so serious for the southern states that "it is
a matter of sincere congratulations that the sanitary
branch of the Federal government is so fully alive to the
dangers . . . and has taken decisive steps toward prevent-
ing its spread."

The federal government had in fact been at work
against yellow fever since the establishment by its National
Board of Health of a Havana Yellow Fever Commission in

1879, of which Sternberg had been secretary. Other members were a Dr. Chaille of New Orleans; Thomas Hardee, a civil engineer; Juan Guiteras, a Cuban refugee professor; and Rudolph Matas, then a medical student. The commission had been told to study the sanitary conditions of the principal ports in Cuba from which shipments were made to the United States, the pathology of the disease, and its so-called endemicity. The frightful wave of yellow fever that swept the lower central valley of North America from New Orleans up the Ohio River demanded that something be done.

In Cuba, Dr. Carlos Finlay was among the prominent physicians who became involved with this board. The son of a Scottish doctor and a Parisienne, he had been born in Cuba, but sent to France for his early schooling. He graduated from the Jefferson Medical College in 1855, spoke at least four languages, and was an honest and dedicated man who chose to practice ophthalmology and general medicine in Havana rather than to settle into a well-rewarded practice in New York. He was much impressed with the report that the fever was transmissible, that the agent was in the air, that no one had a second attack, and that its course was self-limited. He thought that if the disease was indeed airborne, it must be transmitted by the household mosquito—then called *Culex fasciatus*, but now *Aëdes aegypti*. In this he was correct, but he did not suspect any change in the transferred material, and he believed that the mosquito's bill acted like a dirty needle, conveying the disease as a dirty hypodermic needle conveys hepatitis.

From 1881 until 1898 Finlay and his faithful disciple Delgado conducted 104 experiments in which he had mosquitoes bite yellow-fever victims and then bite immigrant workers, who probably offered no objection, since it was generally understood that everyone in Havana got the disease sooner or later. No subject was kept behind screens or protected from contact with anyone who had the disease or had been exposed to it. Finlay thought that the mosquito was most infectious right after biting and that

WALTER REED

the sickest patient would be the most likely to transmit the disease. The crucial secret, to be discovered later by the Reed board, was that the female mosquito could get the virus from the victim only in the first two or three days of the disease, and that approximately two weeks had to pass before the virus could multiply sufficiently within the mosquito to enable it to infect a nonimmune person. Another part of the puzzle that escaped Finlay, and Guiteras, and, for a time, Gorgas, was that the severity of the disease affecting the involuntary donor of the virus has nothing to do with the severity experienced by the unlucky recipient.

Why was yellow fever so important to the United States in a time when there were still many pestilences about? It was, simply, the single most dreaded disease in the Americas. Before the turn of the century, every family knew its symptoms; they knew that it might come in the summer and the fall, but would die out with cold weather. Hundreds of thousands of Americans died horribly of the hemorrhaging "Black Vomit," as it was called; and more hundreds of thousands were sickened and terrified, some to the point of madness, according to newspaper accounts. It came in irregular surges, to one area after another, returning just as people were taking hope. It ate its way as randomly and unpredictably through a town as larvae eat through corn or cotton. It seemed to begin at waterfronts and in ports and to jump to dockside taverns and later to houses further inland, finally enveloping a whole community. In some years it moved all the way up the coast, appearing as far north as Philadelphia, New York, and Boston.

It greatly influenced early conquest and settlement of lands in the Carribean and along the coast; probably more than 100,000 people were sacrificed in the nineteenth century in the Spanish attempt to keep Cuba, since the island had yellow fever as its most terrible weapon of defense for at least 150 years before 1900. An epidemic that spread up the Mississippi Valley in 1878 caused an estimated 120,000 cases and 20,000 deaths. Rutherford

Some Medical Advances—and a War

Hayes said in his annual message to the nation that year that yellow fever had brought a "loss to the country . . . to be reckoned by the hundreds of millions of dollars." Interruption of the American trade with and from Cuba continued to be enormously costly.

The disease came on rapidly, sometimes with a single chill. The victim might sense strange excitement and feel dizzy; he might be wakened from sound sleep by a headache violent enough to jerk him, retching, from his bed. His temperature would climb swiftly. Some patients were spared the second stage, which usually lasted about three days, during which the temperature rose, the skin was flushed, the headache became excruciating, and all the muscles and joints ached "as though in a press." There was strenuous nausea and bleeding from the mouth. A terrifying kind of excitement would make the patient seem mad or drunk. About the fifth day there would be a deceptive abatement of symptoms. This was the eye of the hurricane, giving false hope; pain and fever would sub- side, the churning stomach relax, the vise loosen. The patient might sleep and awake refreshed enough to as- sume that the worst was over, but this respite was only the prelude to a final stage, in which toxemia ruined the liver and there would be bleeding from the gastrointestinal tract. Jaundice usually appeared, and the vomiting of blood blackened by digestive enzymes marked the last stage.

When whole cities succumbed to terror, eyewitnesses reported demoralization and despair such as Thucydides or Boccaccio wrote about. This report appeared in J. M. Keating's book *History of Yellow Fever* (1879), which de- scribed the Memphis yellow fever outbreak of 1878:

> An appalling gloom hung over the doomed city. At night it was silent as the grave; by day . . . desolate as the desert . . . the solemn oppression of universal death bore upon the human mind, as if the day of judgment was about to dawn. . . . Not a sound was to be heard. . . . Death pre- vailed everywhere. . . . The poor were reduced to beg- gary, and even the rich gladly accepted alms. . . . A family

of four was found dead . . . the bodies partially
decomposed. . . . Men, women, and children poured out
of the city by every possible avenue of escape. A few
steamboats were filled . . . but mostly shunned . . . by
those who had the means for railroad travel, and had mind
sufficient left to think of the possibility of their becoming
charnelhouses. . . . Out by the country roads to the little
hamlets and plantations . . . out by every possible
conveyance . . . hacks, carriages, wagons, furniture vans,
and street drays . . . batteaux . . . anything that could float
on the river. . . . The cars of the trains for several days
went out literally packed to suffocation with people.

The unconsciously patronizing mind of the present may
see in the yellow fever research many false assumptions
and lame conclusions; but there can be no doubt at all that
the enemy the researchers sought to overcome was viru-
lent enough to have altered today's world had it not been
vanquished.

There was certainly a degree of cooperation among
those early investigators of yellow fever, but little agreement. In 1887–88 Finlay had sent Sternberg cultures that
contained a variety of organisms, and Sternberg did find
Finlay's micrococcus occasionally in victims of yellow
fever; but he decided that it was found everywhere, and
had little to do with the disease under investigation. He
concluded that Finlay was not really a well-trained bacteriologist, but one who would no doubt be proud of anything
he cultured. Before he became surgeon general,
Sternberg concluded that the mosquito theory deserved
little attention.

On November 13, 1897, Sternberg's paper "Recent
Researches Relating to the Etiology and Specific Treatment of Yellow Fever" appeared in *Medical News*. It had
been given at the Twelfth International Medical Congress
in Moscow. In it he pointed to his "bacillus X" as the
causative agent.

Comparative experiments already made at the Army
Medical Museum, by Major Walter Reed . . . show certain
cultural differences between the bacillus icteroides of

Some Medical Advances—and a War

Sanarelli and my bacillus X. Whether these are simply due to the fact that bacillus X has been cultivated for eight years in an artificial [medium], or are to be considered as evidence that we are dealing with two more or less permanent varieties of a single species, or are to be taken as evidence that the bacillus of Sanarelli is specifically distinct from my bacillus X can only be determined by further investigation and especially by comparative experiments reacting to the pathogenic power of the cultures obtained by me from yellow-fever cadavers in Brazil. At present bacillus X is non-motile, while Sanarelli's bacillus is actively motile. But in my original cultures . . . bacillus X was motile.

In his article Sternberg discussed examples of the discovery of bacteria whose relationship to a specific disease was inferred rather than proved. He conceded that if Sanarelli could get firm proof that *Bacillus icteroides* was in truth the yellow fever germ—by producing the disease in five human beings given subcutaneous or intravenous injection of filtered cultures of the same—he would have to accept these results as "demonstrating the specific character of the bacillus."

He added, however, that Sanarelli's bacillus had not been found consistently present in blood and tissues of yellow fever cadavers. The Italians had cited eleven cases, in only six of which had his organism been found. Sanarelli complained of the difficulty of isolating it, partly because of secondary infection. Sternberg had never found secondary infections a problem. The two men engaged in a crossfire of differences, the arguments of both sounding flimsy today for bacteriologists so famous. Dr. T. S. Dabney of New Orleans, another skeptic, wrote in the same issue of the *News* of his disbelief in Sanarelli's claims. But even as the journal appeared, a tablet was being set in place at the University of Siena to note the discovery of the yellow fever germ by its distinguished alumnus.

The same issue of the *News* concluded that the yellow fever epidemic in the Gulf states had, "thanks to the

vigorous enforcement of sanitary and quarantine measures," not reached as far as earlier epidemics, nor had it
been as "alarmingly fatal" as expected—although it killed
300 people and made 1800 sick. It had been useful, the
News went on blandly, in renewing the interest of the
medical community in this disease. It aroused enough
interest in the U.S. Marine Hospital Service to have the
team of Eugene Wasdin and H. D. Geddings sent to
Havana. These two scientists were ardent Sanarelli supporters; they became opponents of Walter Reed and led
the Marine Hospital Service into battle over opposing
theories of yellow fever causation and spread.

A paper published in the *British Medical Journal* on
December 18, 1897, must have engendered great excitement among all the bacteriologists. It announced that Ross
had found that the malarial parasite, the plasmodium,
underwent certain changes in the anopheles mosquito.
This made it seem possible that the parasite was conveyed
by that insect and by no other means, after a suitable
incubation period, and that the parasites went in as blood
came out when the mosquito bit. All the physicians in the
Army Medical School soon became aware of this enormous advance in the understanding of malaria—and of
disease transmission in a more general sense.

Walter Reed must have been deeply interested, but since
on December 20 he stood by his father's new grave, such
scientific matters were not foremost in his mind. A letter
he wrote to Laura had crossed in the mail the one she
wrote about their father's death. It was poignant with his
worry about his family, and with his self-criticism for not
playing a more active part in relieving the needs of his sister
and for not attending his father as his health was failing.

Before long the whole nation was swept up in the furor
of going to war with Spain. Cuba had been a bone of
contention for some time, and a mysterious explosion that
sank the American battleship *Maine* in Havana Harbor in
February 1898 provided as good an occasion as any for
settling the problem once and for all. "Remember the
Maine!" was a battlecry that was heeded across the country

Some Medical Advances—and a War

—and one with immediate consequences for the Army Medical Service.

Reed's friend Jefferson Randolph Kean, who had been transferred to New England, was among those who felt sure that war was at hand. His diary notes that after hearing of the sinking of the *Maine* he had begun to "prepare for war in my studies and other activities." He estimated the number and disposition of the National Guard and army troops that would be stationed on the New England coast and the medical and hospital supplies these men would need. The surgeon general's office thanked him for his report, but "stated that war was not anticipated."

Although Kean's request to be sent to the front when war materialized was denied because he "had shown such an excellent understanding of conditions and needs in New England," that misplaced Virginian was finding that to understand another region of his country was not necessarily to love it. The Boston mind seems to have been less than congenial to the man whose diary began with the statement: "I come of good Virginia ancestry and . . . one maternal progenitor held the . . . position of Secretary of the Colony at Jamestown for some years before that ancestor-and-furniture-laden vessel the Mayflower sailed from Holland." It is perhaps not surprising that when invited in March to a dinner of the Sons of the American Revolution in Boston, and, by some mischance, invited to speak, he took the occasion to point out his disgust that all of the speeches made that night "had reference not to the Revolution where Virginia and Massachusetts fought gloriously side by side, but to an unfortunate family quarrel in which they had discussed a constitutional difference with equal heroism but on opposite sides."

It apparently gave him pleasure to add that he saw "imminent in the near future a war cloud that would bring Massachusetts and Virginia together shoulder to shoulder" . . . and that he . . . "welcomed it both for the sake of bleeding and oppressed Cuba and because it would lead us away from memories of fratricidal strife." He then dropped his membership in the society, and noted later that when war did come, as it did on April 25, it was "a great surprise to the people of Boston, who seemed to think that war was an obsolete procedure and that anyway it could not come until they had been consulted and had a town meeting to consider the matter."

Bostonians were not the only surprised Americans. The Army Medical Corps had only 177 commissioned officers and 750 enlisted members to care for the regular peacetime army of 25,000. When war was declared, all ready elements of the army gathered to attack Santiago, and with one regular medical officer assigned to each regiment, there was virtually nobody left to cope with the needs of the voluntary army that would obviously be required to wage the Spanish-American War. The hasty recall of 15 physicians who had been dismissed as an economy measure four years earlier brought the physician complement up to 192.

The requisite wartime medical corps was quickly marshaled, much as small boys indiscriminately enroll other boys for their war games. The governors chose colonels, and the colonels chose their regiments. The surgeon that a colonel chose might be a good physician, but some who were not seem to have been appointed as well because he was a superb euchre player or raconteur, or simply because he could hold his liquor. He might have been unable to make a living before he got the steady though small pay of an army surgeon. There was little chance that the new men would know much about military medicine or epidemiology. So the army's health was perforce turned over to a hastily enrolled lot of haphazardly trained doctors appointed by political hacks.

Nonetheless, the examinations for admission to the regular medical corps continued rigorous. Albert E. Truby, a successful candidate, has left an impressive account of its difficulty in his *Memoir of Walter Reed*. The examining board of which Reed was a member began its review of the dozens of candidates on a Sunday, and by

Some Medical Advances—and a War

Tuesday thirteen had been dismissed. Then "six had failed the physical . . . seven had failed in anatomy. Others fell down in surgery, and then on Wednesday afternoon . . . a tall, slender officer, very military in appearance, with a serious but kindly face [Reed] . . . took us in hand." Truby was fortunate in having read of the work of Ronald Ross on malaria; he was one of two candidates the board passed.

A month after the United States declared war, its surgeon general lobbed the opening shot of his own war across international boundaries. He attacked Sanarelli in the *Transactions of the Association of American Physicians*, offering correction of his claims and quoting the Italian's sarcastic description of Sternberg's work as "the most recent, the most rich and the most methodical contribution to this disease known up to the present time," and his snide reference to the surgeon general's statement "that the specific microbe of yellow fever is yet to be found."

Sternberg reported that this was not quite his position, repeating what he had said in an earlier report: that "among the micro-organisms encountered there is not one which, by its constant presence and special pathogenic power can be shown indisputably to be the specific infection agent in this disease." He bristled at Sanarelli's claims, indicating that his "mistakes might be excused but it is difficult to attribute the . . . misleading quotation from my report as a simple mistake." Tempers were clearly rising. Nobody likes to have his work challenged, and perhaps scientists of any kind are among the most easily aroused by challenge. Sternberg went on to say that "The unfairness and misleading character of this attempt to rule bacillus X out of court is shown," but that "this fact is suppressed by Dr. Sanarelli." Sternberg wound up in a cold rage, saying "The misrepresentation of the facts as set forth in my published report is unworthy of a scientific man." He then promised that the Army Medical Corps would study Sanarelli's claims. His promise was kept. They were disproved.

Novy, then in the early stage of his distinguished career at the University of Michigan, entered the fray with the statement that:

> The etiology of yellow fever is yet to be worked out. The microbes of Havelburg and Sanarelli are to be placed in the already long list of disproved causes. . . . It is more likely that the germ of yellow fever, as well as those of smallpox, measles, hydrophobia, etc., belongs to a group of organisms, smaller than our bacteria, and as yet unknown, awaiting discovery. The recent work of Roux and Nocard on the microbe of pleuropneumonia already proves the existence of organisms smaller than the "infinitely small" bacteria.

It is interesting that in the midst of all this scientific controversy, set against the background of the threat of war, the question of human experimentation became important. Attacking Sanarelli's claims, Victor Vaughan, a Michigan epidemiologist stated that he thought that his injection of toxin into patients ("I suppose they were patients," he said, "for they were in the hospital") in the hope of identifying the specific germ of yellow fever was "ridiculous." But the great William Osler thought otherwise, saying that "experiments upon men" had been

> . . . characterized by Dr. Vaughan as ridiculous, but I beg to say that that is not the term to use. The limits of human experimentation should be clearly defined in our minds. From a clinical standpoint almost every dose of medicine we give is an experiment. Who knows what may happen from giving a 2-grain dose of quinine to a child? It may die, as did one of Dr. McKenzie's children. To deliberately inject a poison of known high degree of virulency into a human being, unless you obtain that man's sanction, is not ridiculous, it is criminal.

Meanwhile, the medical corps, so pitifully supported and greatly overextended, must have been a great anxiety to Surgeon General Sternberg. He needed his most reliable men in key positions, and when both Kean and Reed asked for assignment to wartime field service, he refused

Some Medical Advances—and a War

their requests. Reed kept his friend informed of what went on in the Washington headquarters, where someone did mention Kean's name in connection with another assignment, and wrote:

> Sure enough your letter . . . had entirely escaped my mind in the rush of business and the mental worry my boy, Lawrence, had given me by his determination to enlist for a commission in the regular Army. . . . I might as well tell you that Dr. Sternberg is trying to keep all non-immune medical officers out of Cuba. He doesn't propose to let Hall remain at Key West, if yellow fever should appear there. Hoff has been given charge of a ship of 500 beds. Col. Bache thought you might like to be one of his assistants. . . . I am afraid, dear Doctor, that the mere accident of station will keep you and myself out of active service. I volunteered for field service weeks ago, and begged that I might be assigned to Duty [duty always had a capital D for Walter Reed] with Captain Sampson's squadron. To all of which, the S.G. turned a deaf ear.

The lamentably small medical corps had to be responsible for much more than battle wounds. The *Journal of the American Medical Association* pointed out that "During the past two months we have heard of the danger from yellow fever in the invasion of Cuba, but nothing has been said of the future possibilities of a disease which during our Civil War affected every newly raised regiment soon after it went into camp. Typhoid fever was the camp fever of the Civil War . . . a deadly disease." It was natural that the army's problems with disease control should be as pressing as those of combat. It was the only agency that drew large numbers of men from every corner of the country, herded them together under conditions that were necessarily seldom sanitary, and thus not only pooled all America's infectious diseases but provided ideal conditions for their culture. Also, since manpower was the army's prime weapon, a sick man was a severe liability. Today's public, shocked from time to time by news of such army projects as nerve gas, would do well to remember how much it owes the Army Medical Corps.

WALTER REED

Although historically typhus and typhoid fever had long been confused, a paper by Gerhard of Philadelphia in the *American Journal of the Medical Sciences* in 1837 had given a complete account of the features that differentiate the two diseases. Typhus, spread by lice, is a disease of crowding, winter, war, refugees, and poverty. Typhoid, filth-borne, depends on the ingestion of particles of contaminated fecal material clinging to dirty hands or linen or suspended in water or milk. It may be conveyed by person-to-person contact also, or by flies crawling on food after crawling on contaminated material. It occurs in the autumn, most commonly in the young, and more often among men than women. It confers immunity that is by no means total. The organism is killed by heat of 60° C., but not by cold; it may actually be recovered from the ice on rivers or ponds. Seafood, especially oysters, may spread it, and contaminated soil will remain contaminated for some time.

It was known that it could be largely eliminated by isolating the sick and carefully disposing of anything they had contaminated; and purification of water and establishment of sewage systems all but eradicated it wherever such sophisticated measures were taken. Sternberg knew what precautions to take, and sent official directives requiring all medical officers to keep the camps hygienic. But their role was more of an advisory one than one of authority, and line officers regarded such orders as unfeasible, and even ridiculed them. A few smart commanding officers took advantage of medical knowledge, but the scene was nonetheless set for disaster.

It was common to diagnose the sickness of any soldier as measles, mumps, or chicken pox, of which there was plenty. Or officers, not wanting the scandal of typhoid, strongly encouraged calling the illness dysentery, malaria, or acute indigestion. Sometimes it *was* acute indigestion, since this was the first war in which an attempt was made to supply the men with refrigerated meat—in the Civil War meat accompanied the army on the hoof and was slaughtered and eaten on the spot—and not only was there much spoilage, but in the war with Spain, it was claimed, the meat was carted about in wagons also used for hauling manure and garbage, which were never cleaned. The canned beef was putrid more often than not, and New York's two leading newspapers made much of what they called the Bully Beef Scandal. But the basic medical problem of the military was bad sanitation. Ninety percent of the regiments had typhoid fever within a few months.

Walter Reed had become accustomed to ironical turns of events. Nonetheless, he must have felt angry frustration when he was refused a mission in Havana while his son Lawrence—soon to be twenty-one—having been denied a commission, enlisted in the army, from which he would ultimately retire as major general after forty-two years in service. Reed himself was told to concentrate on "whether or not the government should issue the so-called 'cholera bands' for the use of the U.S. troops in the field." Cholera bands were a sort of Ace bandage with which to bind the abdomen of one dying of cholera, which were without any effect whatsoever!

CHAPTER VII

A First Look at Cuba

Although the Spanish-American War lasted but a few months, 20,738 cases of typhoid fever were recorded among the first 171,000 American soldiers collected to fight. The death toll was 1,500; the fatality rate for the stricken, 7.6 percent. It was clear that in spite of misdiagnosis, coverups, and a more zealous doctoring of statistics than of patients, the real killer that year was the typhoid bacillus. This was seen as a scandal, and the surgeon general sent his trusted troubleshooter, Walter Reed, along with a team of experts on contract, to find out what had happened. E. O. Shakespeare and Victor Vaughan were on the typhoid board chaired by Reed. Major George Hopkins was originally one of the board—later called the commission—but seems to have been phased out. At the time of its establishment under orders of the secretary of war on August 18, recruits were still streaming into camps in the extreme summer heat, and some were still dying of fevers in a war that was already concluded, for the Spanish had signed a peace agreement in mid-August.

The board was charged with studying the conditions in camps in the States. It began to seem that Reed would never get to Cuba. But the men assigned him were excellent and worthy of his respect and friendship. Vaughan, dean of Ann Arbor's medical school, was one of the leaders in the country in the field of public health, and Shakespeare was widely recognized for leadership in epidemiology. One of his early investigations had located the source of a typhoid fever epidemic in Plymouth, Pennsylvania, where excreta from a typhoid victim, thrown on a snowy hillside, had contaminated the city's water supply; and he had represented the United States in a study of cholera in Spain in 1885.

Happily, the board was supplied with a means of transportation, a place to stay, and considerable comfort when the president of the Southern Railroad put his private railroad car at its disposal. Although the investigators waded daily through the filth of army camps, they returned each night to a Pullman car, that most sybaritic accommodation of the period. The kitchen was presided over by a chef such as only the rich could afford; an attentive porter—a combination of valet and therapist in those days—made their beds and met every request; and competent military stenographers dealt with their copious notes. The fore part of the Pullman was an office and reception room, and each man had his own bedroom. Such luxury must have given the men great pleasure, but there was one drawback—the noisiness of the switchyards near army camps, where the moving of supplies went on all night and caused insomnia. At Jacksonville this problem was overcome by Gen. Fitzhugh Lee's order that the car be stationed near his own quarters, where relative silence prevailed.

When their trip began at Camp Alger, on the Potomac in Virginia, they were brought face to face with the complete absence of any laboratory or microscope. Their diagnosis of typhoid would have to depend on clinical assessment. They decided to examine every patient they could in every camp they visited; to inspect every well; and to list the sick by military unit, noting the places from which they had come. They would then determine the extent of typhoid infection throughout each camp, using a sort of grid they designed to indicate when each population had arrived and whence it had come.

They found the medical corps in a sorry state. Some of the military surgeons, as well as some of the newly commissioned military officers, were bewildered by camp life. They were untrained in the keeping of records and unaware of the various forms a single disease could take. And although many had had typhoid fever, they failed to recognize it when it assailed their noses. The authorities in Camp Alger reported much typhomalaria and malaria in cases where the diagnosis should have been typhoid. The myth of typhomalaria had been fostered by the publication in 1863 of Woodward's *Outlines of the Chief Camp Diseases in the United States Armies*, the bible of military medicine. But even some contract surgeons who were virtually unqualified for their jobs were aware that quinine was good in malaria but did nothing in typhoid. The Gruber-Widal reaction had been introduced to determine a diagnosis of typhoid in 1896, but it was hardly in general use and required a microscope in any case. The presence of malaria could be readily determined by finding the plasmodia in the blood, but few physicians knew how to make the blood smears needed.

The board was seldom received gracefully by state-appointed colonels and their untrained, newly appointed army surgeons. Since they resisted the board's insistence that many of their patients had typhoid fever, it was necessary to convince them by sending those patients away for diagnosis at other hands. Fifty were sent at first, and later 150 were sent to Washington and then to the best hospitals in Baltimore, Philadelphia, New York, Boston, and Cleveland. To the fury of the colonels and their appointees, they were all found to have typhoid, and none had malaria. Such vindication did little to ensure a more cordial reception for the board, which went next to Florida.

Its itinerary included Fernandina; Camp Cuba Libre near Jacksonville; Camp George H. Thomas in Georgia; and Camp Meade near Harrisburg, Pennsylvania. An extra stint, not included in either the board's original charge or in its final report, took the investigators to Montauk Point on Long Island, where the Fifth Army Corps had just returned from Cuba. Before long, Sternberg ordered the establishment of diagnostic laboratories in all the camps.

At Cuba Libre the group found fecal material being carelessly disposed of—and 1,030 cases of typhoid. In the Second Division fecal material was taken in open tubs to be scattered near company roads; in the nine regiments of this division there were ultimately 2,092 cases of typhoid that had been misdiagnosed as typhomalaria or acute indigestion. Camp doctors were indignant at the board's insistence that camp sanitation might have something to do with all that sickness—and that the sickness was typhoid.

At Jacksonville the board gave a graphic demonstration that the filth of the camp was being brought directly into contact with food; they sprinkled lime over feces deposited by the wayside, and within five minutes saw flies move over the soldiers' food, leaving white trails of lime. The Third Nebraska, at Jacksonville, was the regiment of William Jennings Bryan, a colonel for the occasion, and always Walter Reed's bête noire. It must have given Reed secret pleasure to have to lecture the Golden Orator on the lack of sanitation in his area. Later, when Fitzhugh Lee reviewed the troops, he insisted that the members of the board all join him on his decorated stand to give a jaunty salute to the colonel from Nebraska.

The problem at Chickamauga was all too evident. The ground was too hard for latrines, and Vaughan was to say in his memoirs: "I have never seen so large an area of fecal-stained soil as . . . in Chickamauga Park in 1898. . . . The woody lands were smeared with alvine discharges . . .

A First Look at Cuba

one could not walk under the trees without soiling one's shoes with human excrement. . . . An occasional rain was sinking the pollution below the surface and down into the soil where the typhoid bacilli may retain their vitality and virulence for a long time."

The attitude of the officers and the hopeless living conditions of the men can be understood when it is remembered that everything was in a holding pattern. Since the signing of the peace treaty in August, morale was at an abysmal low. By September, lacking any motivation and wrung by homesickness and fever, the troops were completely demoralized. As regiments moved, they left the grounds teeming with infection, and incoming regiments made no effort to clean things up, but pitched their tents directly over partially covered latrines. Moreover, the horrified members of the board would see untrained and clumsy orderlies soiling themselves with bedpans and the bedding of the sick, only to pass food at table without having washed.

At Chickamauga the board had a chance to establish the incubation period for typhoid fever when fifty healthy nurses from Chicago began work in the hospitals. The first came down with typhoid ten days after arrival. Unfortunately, nothing was done to protect the other nurses exposed to the sick, but the board's conclusion that the incubation period was ten days, more or less, has stood the test of time. At its last stop, Camp Meade, the board found matters gratifyingly reflecting its recommendations, which apparently were beginning to impress soldiers as well as physicians.

On October 19 Walter Reed was summarily taken from his important and useful work for an order almost as unwelcome as that to assess cholera bands. Sternberg wanted him to go to Natural Bridge, Virginia, to make recommendations about the possibility of converting the big resort hotel there into a military hospital. Reed had begun going over the typhoid charts and figures with Shakespeare and Vaughan, but now the two had to continue without him. The army was under pressure to keep sick soldiers in military installations, and there was need for another large facility. There had been a scandal when soldiers from Cuba overran a hospital in Montauk, Long Island, and spread fear of the contagion. One serendipitous gain from the trip to Natural Bridge was a visit Reed managed with his brother James in nearby Lynchburg. Walter seems not to have been in very good physical condition at the time, but he must have enjoyed reminiscing about old times and familiar places. When he returned to Washington he found a letter from his son telling him that the Second Artillery, to which Lawrence belonged, was being sent to Cuba.

Shakespeare and Vaughan, meanwhile, tabulated data with the part-time help of an enlisted clerk, working at the Army Medical Museum, and taking work home at night to their rooms on K Street. They carefully searched the daily and monthly sick reports of 118 regiments, located the site in camp of every tent in which a sick man had slept, and read charts and records from every camp, large or small, north or south. They learned whether or not typhoid had been present in the place from which each soldier had come. They learned the story of every man who had reported any fever or diarrhea during the entire Spanish-American War and for a time thereafter. Compulsively they examined case histories, and even followed soldiers into civilian hospitals all over the country. One hospital in Chicago gave them trouble, but they "appealed to the members of the medical staff, prominent Chicago physicians, and they, at their own expense in both time and money, supplied . . . the data."

It is probably natural enough that Vaughan, who wrote a history of these times, and who became a distinguished elder statesman in medicine, should be remembered before Reed in connection with this work. He was named as the sole author of a report about the board in the *American Journal of Medical Science* in 1899, and again, when it was published in *Transactions of the Association of American Physicians*. Vaughan emphasized that he had permission

A First Look at Cuba

from his colleagues and the surgeon general, and that the paper was incomplete.

Vaughan's autobiography explains that he and Shakespeare were discharged from the army for reasons of economy in June 1899, but they divided up the remaining sick reports and worked on them at home. They were planning a temporary resurrection of the board in 1900 when Major Shakespeare suddenly died. Reed's *Abstract* of the board's report was published by the government, but Vaughan felt "that a bare statement of our conclusions without supporting evidence would not be convincing." He observed that by then Reed was "carrying out his brilliant and successful researches on the transmission of yellow fever" and added, "Thank God! he lived long enough to see this work accepted and his name written among the great benefactors of his race."

The story of the various publications is quite incomplete. The original brief summary in the form of a letter was first published during World War II. The document of special importance relating to the typhoid study was Reed's *Abstract* of the report published in 1900, with an introduction by Sternberg and a letter of transmittal from Walter Reed. The conclusions of this *Abstract* appear in an essay on "The Etiology of Typhoid Fever" by Walter Reed. Two of Vaughan's papers for which he is listed as sole author are an almost literal copying of the *Abstract* of the report, which according to Stanhope Bayne-Jones, was written by Reed. There was no acknowledgment in Vaughan's papers, written after Reed and Shakespeare had died, that the work had been that of a group consisting of himself, Walter Reed, and E. O. Shakespeare.

An odd footnote to all this can be found in Ashburn's history of the medical corps, in which he was so confused by or unacquainted with the findings of the board that he claimed it overlooked the existence of typhoid carriers. The delineation of the carrier state by the board did not, it is true, have the impact it should have had, although it was recorded with crystal clarity. At that time, only diphtheria carriers had been recognized. Such transmission from people without symptoms probably accounted for the appearance of a typhoid epidemic apparently de novo. Previously carriers had not been considered.

Vaughan later showed vexation at what he apparently saw as a slight to him and wrote: "I admit that I was somewhat irritated by a statement . . . from the Surgeon General's office about the close of the World War saying that we had no medical report on the Spanish-American War and not mentioning the work of the Typhoid Commission. . . . An official report of our medical histories that makes no mention of the work of the Typhoid Commission is certainly defective and in memory of Majors Reed and Shakespeare I enter a protest." And Jefferson Kean took up the cudgels on behalf of Reed, then dead for a decade, when he wrote in 1912 about statements in the *Journal of the American Medical Association*: "The board which investigated the origin and spread of typhoid fever in the U.S. Military Camps in 1898 had as its president, Maj. Walter Reed, U.S.A., of yellow fever fame, and not Dr. Victor C. Vaughan of the University of Michigan." As it happened, when the full report of the commission appeared, it was 1904, and by then Vaughan was the only survivor. The full official report was listed with Walter Reed, Victor Vaughan, and E. O. Shakespeare as its authors.

Besides producing such differences about attribution of credit, the report of the board did a great deal to overcome prevailing false beliefs about typhoid fever. It was used widely by public health workers and by military surgeons the world over. It demonstrated that failure to heed the rules of sanitation in the field led to the contamination of the camps, that defecation and urination near living and eating areas spread the disease. The board incriminated feces, filth, fingers, and flies, in that order, and reduced the emphasis on water as an agent of contamination. A serious outbreak of typhoid continued into the fall of 1900, and had the board not continued to clarify

A First Look at Cuba

and enforce sanitary regulations, typhoid victims would have been much more numerous than they were.

In the spring of 1899 the Spaniards were no longer a threat in Cuba, but diseases were, and now the United States had some responsibility there. General Sternberg secured from the secretary of War the appointment of a medical board to pursue "scientific investigations of acute infectious diseases prevalent on the island of Cuba." He appointed Walter Reed its presiding officer. What began with reference to infectious diseases in general, and typhoid fever in particular, soon turned to the control of yellow fever. And a very good thing that was, in view of what was taking place on that tropical island. Others appointed to the commission were James Carroll, who had been Reed's faithful assistant so long, and two men who were already in Cuba, the American Jesse Lazear and the Cuban Aristides Agramonte.

During the previous year the Marine Hospital Service had published a marvelous compilation of bizarre notions about yellow fever, combined with some shrewd deductions about it, which simply reflected the bewilderment most respected scientists felt about the malady. One suggestion it made was that a swollen upper lip is a significant diagnostic clue; even Juan Guiteras, an acting assistant surgeon, held that the appearance in the face of waves of jaundice—presumably a kind of yellow aurora borealis—indicated yellow fever. The absence of any standard treatment led to the recommendation of high colonic enemas, sometimes very cool, and the use of turpentine, cocaine, oil catharsis, and diet modification—almost anything that came to mind. Past Assistant Surgeon H. D. Geddings held forth tautologically on the desirability of "therapeutic treatment," as though all treatments were not designed to be therapeutic.

Eugene Wasdin thought the infection probably entered the body via the respiratory organs. J. B. White emphasized the need to stop a beginning epidemic by isolating patients at the outset. But the notions of Henry Rose

Carter, although only partly helpful then, were evidence of his continuing curiosity that was ultimately to contribute to the control of yellow fever. He was convinced of the advantages of isolation, but had no confidence in the disinfection of baggage, the inspection of trains, and all the other measures taken in the belief that the yellow fever organism remained in any material a victim had touched, and that it lay in wait there for the next victim.

Carter, a Southern gentleman who had graduated from the University of Virginia in engineering, had entered medicine when he found that a leg injured in the Civil War was too great a handicap for a civil engineer. He then went into the Marine Hospital Service. He always insisted that he was entitled to little credit for the Reed board's achievement; whenever it was mentioned in the presence of Reed and Carter, each would bow to the other. But without Carter's studies, Reed's search might have taken a different direction. Carter was persistently curious about how yellow fever could appear on a ship that had been at sea for two or more weeks without any sickness aboard. In 1898 he wrote that the space of time before a person fell ill after some mysterious contact with the source of the disease should be examined. The organism must be maturing *somewhere* during that interval, which came to be known as the period of extrinsic incubation. And Carter was right.

It is self-evident that if the organism lurked in materials with which yellow fever patients had been in contact, the way to get rid of the fever was to get rid of the dangerous materials. This might involve burning a whole city (as was done in Siboney, Cuba, a town in which a number of houses were burned in an effort to check the spread of an epidemic that some authorities later concluded had been dengue fever rather than yellow fever) in the false hope of quenching an epidemic. The belief, therefore, had many practical and economic complications. The scientists classified all contaminated material under the term *fomites*, the plural of a Latin word meaning "tinder" (correctly pro-

A First Look at Cuba

nounced to rhyme approximately with "show it days"). The most dramatic—and horrifying—of Reed's experiments would deal with fomites.

Carter had believed in the fomites theory until in June 1888 a Norwegian barque docked at Ships Island, having put out from Rio de Janeiro on May 20 after leaving there a couple of crew members sick with yellow fever. A crew member already ailing when they left port soon got the fever, as did the ship's master, who died of it. Thirteen days out of port the crew began to sicken; many vomited blood and died quickly. The pattern was repeated again and again. There would be a primary case or two around the time of departure, and after an interval of two or three weeks at sea, several crew members would fall sick. And yet, not once in a hundred years had a baggage inspector contracted yellow fever after going through what should logically be considered dangerous material impregnated with something that conveyed yellow fever. Carter found the safety of the baggage handlers fascinating. Carrying out his interest in the space of time, he had some colleagues collect data in a Mississippi town on "the time of the taking down with yellow fever of the first case in any home and the interval elapsing until the taking down of the next case, and so on, in regard to all the members of the family."

Carter's choice of a small, rather remote town for this study was calculated. He had had difficulty "in getting correct, truthful statements from people in towns, where commercial interests were involved." It would be naive to suppose that the public is always ready to cooperate with measures taken for the public weal. Especially at a time when quarantine was sometimes enforced by arms, epidemiologists could have a rough road to travel in getting accurate information from people interested for any reason in concealing it. "The findings from the Mississippi town established . . . that yellow fever is not directly transferable from the sick to the well, but is indirectly transferable through an environment infected by the patient. . . .

The material leaving the person of the patients must undergo . . . some change in the environment before it is capable of infecting another man."

Walter Reed eventually said that observations made by him confirmed Carter's conclusion. In short, the intermediate host was the mosquito. After the mosquito had bitten a person during the first three days of an attack of yellow fever and changes occurred, this liberated the virus so that after about twelve to fourteen days the mosquito was able to transmit the disease.

It was indeed a battle among giants that Reed found himself engaged in. An article of which he was the senior author (and Carroll the second) appeared in *Medical News* in 1899 under the title "Bacillus Icteroides and Bacillus Cholerae Suis—a Preliminary Note." In this he ventured "to express an opinion that the bacillus icteroides (Sanarelli) is a variety of the hog-cholera bacillus . . . only . . . a secondary invader in yellow fever. We find that bacillus X (Sternberg) presents marked differences from the foregoing micro-organisms both as regards its biologic character as well as its pathogenic action toward animals." Sternberg's discomfiture over such rejection of his Bacillus X by a member of his staff was no doubt somewhat reduced by the fact that whatever it was that caused yellow fever was now acknowledged to be too minute for ready recognition under a microscope, and in any case the Reed-Carroll work gave him further ammunition for a vigorous attack on Sanarelli in the same journal. In that year, Dr. Herman Biggs—the great authority of the period on antitoxin and vaccines, who was known to be a cautious man—extolled in the *Medical Record* the virtues of a serum Sanarelli had developed from his *Bacillus icteroides* "for public prophylaxis." And Alin Doty, the health officer of the port of New York, was reported in the *Medical Record* to be concocting a vaccine of his own based on the Sanarelli research.

Sanarelli even claimed that Reed and Carroll had carelessly confused their cultures. In what was evidently a reply to some expression of support, Reed wrote to Dr.

A First Look at Cuba

Harvey Cushing, declaring that "At that time we had no culture of the hog cholera bacillus in our laboratory, nor had we ever worked with it," and offering to send Cushing some cultures for his own inspection. Presumably this authority would be beyond any accusation of a laboratory mix up of cultures. The findings supported Reed. A twenty-three page report he wrote with Carroll, appearing in the *Medical News* of September 9, 1899, took spirited issue with the claim that their laboratory had been careless. It bore the title "The Specific Cause of Yellow Fever. A Reply to Dr. G. Sanarelli."

From all this controversy Reed had a brief respite when he sailed to Cuba on a Ward Line steamer, though as usual he was terribly seasick. He came to expect the loss of about five pounds on the four-day trip from New York to Havana—a loss he could ill afford, since his normal weight was between 140 and 150 pounds. His son Lawrence was already in Cuba and had reported that the heat there was as bad as that of Washington. He had repeatedly asked his father to intercede to help him gain an officer's commission, and Reed must have done so, for Lawrence wrote his father that "The letter you wrote Capt. S. about me was received while the Capt. was on a little tute [*sic*]." The bibulous Capt. S. was known to Reed, and it was he who brought Lawrence out of his quarters at Vedado for a joyous reunion with his father, who described their visit in a letter to his wife:

He [Capt. S] was the same old Schenck as ever and delighted to see me. Yelled for "Serg't. Reed" like a bull roaring. Here came the dear boy, smiling and looking the very picture of health! . . . The Captain gave him a 24 hour pass, so down town we went & had a nice lunch together of chicken salad, beefsteak, etc.! You ought to have seen him eat! Appetite? Stand off! Then we went down Obispo Street & got something for Mother and Little Sister, & then came down to the dock & took the steam launch & came over to the Missouri—He will spend the night with me—Is now Battery Quartermaster Sergeant —ranks next to the 1st Sergeant—& is perfectly happy and contented. His camp is a beautiful one—never saw a better—don't worry about him in that regard. We hope to leave here, tomorrow afternoon, for Nuevitas & then return to Havana—Everything seems promising for a pleasant trip—Darboy [Lawrence] sends you & dear little Sister all Manner of love—I never saw him looking so well & he has enjoyed strolling & talking with his daddie more than I can tell you. I got your letter written on Friday —Hope this will find you back at home—Love & kisses for my precious babies—Must go back on deck to talk to the dear boy—am very well—Devotedly, "Papa."

Reed's good friend Kean, now temporary colonel, was also in Cuba, and he had been there long enough to be aware of all that had been happening, particularly to learn about the concentration camps set up by the Spanish governor, Valeriano Weyler. Indignation at the conditions in these camps had contributed to America's entry into the war. Kean wrote:

> The rich country was all laid waste and deserted except as an occasional fortified village protected by a block house with barbed wire [remains]. It was the first time that I had ever seen . . . barbed wire for entrenchments.
>
> Guines was one of the towns into which Captain Gen. Weyler had collected the country population in his policy of reconcentration. As he made no effective arrangements to feed them they perished . . . from starvation and disease. Of the 14,000 reconcentrados at Guines, 11,000 were reported to have perished. I saw at the Municipal Hospital about a hundred of these poor creatures dying of consumption and in a state of utter destitution.

Kean was having his problems at Marianao trying to install a practical sewer system in an effort to overcome the typhoid that persisted there. The pipes the engineers brought in lay around for months, and when they were finally installed, the discharge end was higher than the input end, and thus, they could not empty. Kean gleefully reported that the Board of Survey, of which he was a member, had used "such vigorous and picturesque language that there was some talk of bringing us before a Court martial for disrespect." It must have been a great

A First Look at Cuba

help to him when Reed came, for Reed had been charged with locating any "neglect on the part of medical officers to make proper sanitary recommendations, or of Commanding Officers to enforce such regulations or of Quartermasters to supply the necessary shelter and appliances for the protection of the health of our troops."

Always obliged to carry out some grand and demanding plan from a personal position of anxiety and virtual poverty, Reed sadly reported to Laura in the spring of 1899 that his help must be limited, for "when I looked at my Bank account . . . it was less than $10! . . . But who ever knew a Reed to have any 'spare change'? Not I, nor you!" And this usually uncomplaining man noted that he had "Never worked so hard in all my life."

The situation of Lawrence, who had not suffered in silence the inequities and discomforts of life in the military, continued to occupy his mind with the helpless regret all loving parents feel when a child is undergoing a period of disappointment and self-doubt. Shortly after their happy reunion in Cuba, Reed learned that Lawrence was transferring to a new battery, having come to the wry and disenchanted conclusion that "a man is a man, and it matters not whether he is a soldier or an officer he still is the same old man." Walter Reed, for whom sea travel was always such an ordeal, did not then know that the next year would involve him in a virtual shuttle between Washington and Cuba.

Walter Reed as a young lieutenant, taken in Harrisonburg, Virginia, 1876, during his honeymoon. *(Courtesy, National Library of Medicine, Bethesda, Md., and William Blinco.)*

Reed in his thirties (1880s), with the mustache he would continue to wear from that time on. *(Courtesy, National Library of Medicine, Bethesda, Md.)*

Maj. Walter Reed in uniform in the late 1890s. *(Courtesy National Library of Medicine, Bethesda, Md.)*

Walter Reed in major's uniform, showing the Maltese Cross
of the U.S. Army Medical Corps. This is the last known
photograph taken of him. *(Courtesy, National Library of Medicine,
Bethesda, Md.)*

CHAPTER VIII

Danger and Disappointment

O ne might suppose that the solving of a medical puzzle is a straight-line enterprise: that it simply involves consistent work, the discarding of failed hypotheses, and an eye set squarely on a common objective. But such work is often sidetracked by someone's persistent adherence to one false belief or another, and much time is lost when an adherent to such a false belief develops ever more sophisticated methods of treatment or prophylaxis based upon it and puts them to trial. Moreover, public interest in and support for this kind of work waxes and wanes, and false claims reduce public trust. Certainly such confusion and lack of discernible progress characterized the yellow fever research.

The trials of Sanarelli's prophylactic serum, although disappointing, failed to discredit belief that the *Bacillus icteroides* was the culprit; and the New York serum had its day. At times it must have seemed that the goal was in sight. The dogged Finlay, so eager to conquer the scourge

WALTER REED

of his adopted people, had correctly implicated the mosquito as vector in a paper published in 1879—but his paper was laced with so many misconceptions and so much recanting that no one could take him seriously. True, by 1879 he had ceased to believe that the fever arose from the generation of a mysterious vegetable-animal organism by conditions of weather and the soil, but he thought that a generation of insects must separate the one that bit a diseased person from the one that conveyed the critical organism to someone else.

Moreover, the public was tired of hearing about nightmare, and longed for a sunnier view of things. This mood was reenforced readily by the press. In June the *Medical Record* quoted General Wood—how accurately we have no way of knowing—as saying while on a visit to Washington:

> There is no yellow fever in the province and no other contagious disease. . . . Santiago is all right. All we want is a chance to earn an honest living down there and an opportunity to go to school [sic], and we'll get along. There is no illness to speak of in the whole province. The death rate there, . . . lower than . . . in New York or Philadelphia, . . . is about 14 in 1,000. . . . Yellow fever is virtually stamped out and there are no indications of its return. This is the first summer in the history of the province when there has not been some.

The article was headed "A Transformed Santiago," and in it Wood attributed the transformation to his insistence "that the people shall take a bath once in a while, that the vaults shall be drained and whitewashed, and that houses and yards shall be kept cleansed, . . . all the streets drained in ditches, and the drainage . . . carried away." He did admit that several cases of the fever had been reported within the week, but the article was in every other particular gratifying to the naive American faith in soap and water and clean living.

Even Sternberg felt the new confidence. His paper, "The Report of the Commission Appointed by the President to Investigate the Conduct of the War Department in the War with Spain," held that . . .

. . . yellow fever could fairly easily be controlled. Yellow fever, as it prevailed in Cuba, was of a mild type and its mortality rate was low. That its outbreak might have been prevented by the burning of all houses at Siboney, and by more complete isolation of the Cuban and Spanish refugees is a question, but certainly the chances of avoiding the anticipated and much dreaded disease would have been increased had such measures been adopted. That it was kept out of our coast cities is due to the watchfulness of national and local quarantine officers and to the establishment and maintenance of a detention camp at Montauk.

This period of complacent confidence in what sanitation and American ingenuity could accomplish was short-lived. By July 12 Leonard Wood was writing in some consternation to a friend in New York about an outbreak of yellow fever "confined entirely to the American residents of the city [Havana]." He still thought the fever was a disease of the unclean and that sanitation would prevent it, and he moved the troops inland to "points at which Yellow Fever has never originated." He noted that the death rate among military officers was very heavy: "everyone who has taken it has died." And he spoke of having since his arrival been "on the jump trying to establish the absolutely necessary measures which should have been established two weeks ago (confidentially)." He then made rather puzzling reference to "the unwashed American element," drifters, perhaps, that he was arresting, scrubbing, disinfecting, and shipping out of the country. He realized that tying "the whole place up with a cast-iron military order" was going to cause "a great deal of kicking," but he felt confident that it would save many lives. Gen. George Andrews sent out orders from the headquarters of the Department of Santiago that reflected Wood's anxiety. The yellow jack—a flag warning that there was yellow fever aboard ship—went up. The bars were closed, and everything was scrubbed up in a frantic and unavailing effort to hold off the disease by improved sanitation.

Meanwhile, the controversy over its causative agent and the way it spread continued. In August the *Medical News* noted that in spite of the many claims, "the etiology of the disease remains in doubt," and "there still remain a number of experienced bacteriologists who do not consider Sanarelli's bacillus as the specific cause." Wasdin and Geddings, of the Marine Hospital Service, were unwavering in their belief in Sanarelli; their publication of the Wasdin-Geddings Report in August 1899 was a dark blot on the record of what became later the United States Public Health Service. It was widely read and approved, and it helped turn the war against a common enemy into a conflict among the several arms of government. Wasdin chauvinistically attacked the army, and he began looking on Walter Reed as his natural enemy. The report concluded that "infection takes place by way of the respiratory tract" and that "colonization in the lungs is followed by a 'secondary infection.' "

The fall of 1899 must have been a low point for Walter Reed. The views about yellow fever that opposed his had gained wide acceptance, and the army again turned him into a chore boy just when he began to feel the stature of demonstrated usefulness in his field. Maybe he would go down to posterity simply as a contributor to the work of the Typhoid Board. Of course, there was the Reed trough, but however useful this might be—and it was useful—this was not something a Virginia gentleman would happily point to on many occasions as the crown of his life's work. The trough was a contrivance to deal with the safe disposal of the enormous amount of human waste put out by soldiers in crowded camps. It was a galvanized iron trough from which waste was "emptied by an odorless excavating apparatus consisting of a water-tight tank . . . carried on a strongly constructed wagon bed." It had been used successfully at Camp Meade, Pennsylvania, and in camps near San Francisco.

The unprecedented elevation of a member of the Army Medical Corps, Leonard Wood, to the post of governor general showed what heights a man (but always another man) might reach. It cost Reed something to write Wood a letter of congratulation, thinking of all that he himself was

Danger and Disappointment

expected to do without adequate staff or time, and how natural it was for the surgeon general to send him on relatively trivial errands. He was probably far too modest to realize that his prepossessing, gentlemanly, and militarily correct appearance and his diplomatic Southern speech made him an excellent envoy for the harassed Sternberg, who himself betrayed a twinge or two of jealousy over the elevation of the gifted Wood.

At fifty Reed was slim—perhaps too slim. He remained militarily erect, but he was greying, and he was always weary and betrayed his exhaustion sometimes in ways alarming to his family. But the thought of rebellion never entered his head. This minister's son, this Victorian man, had been trained to obey and to conform, and although he was capable of merriment and a vigorous enjoyment of life, he was without an instinct for self-aggrandizement strong enough to divert him from the path before him.

Among his seemingly pedestrian assignments was one that sent him to Fort Thomas to deal with the scandal there over the condition of men returning from Cuba. The *Cincinnati Enquirer* was running headlines that screamed about the emaciated condition of these "once sturdy men." The reputation of the Army Medical Corps needed Reed to shore it up. In February 1900 he was appointed to a board that met in Washington to examine paymasters, and when he was reassigned to Cuba in March it was to investigate the use of electrozone as a disinfectant. Because the Americans found themselves faced with the necessity of cleaning up Havana again and again, they wanted more information about this scheme of passing an electric current through sea water to liberate some of the chlorine for germicidal purposes. Truby tells of meeting Reed in Havana and hearing his conclusion that electrozone was "more expensive and less efficient . . . than a solution made with ordinary chloride of lime."

Reed may have been on a dull and fruitless mission in Havana, but he managed to find congenial company there with whom to spend some very happy hours. He lived for some time at Columbia Barracks with other medical officers. Truby indicates that the younger men were at first somewhat intimidated, "but he was jovial and soon put us at ease. He knew how to join in with young doctors and share in their jokes and amusements." He spent considerable time with Lazear in his laboratory, and discussed yellow fever when visiting physicians and others dropped in on the pleasant evening gatherings on the Barracks veranda.

In view of his later premature and tragic death, one cannot think of Lazear without great sadness. He was from all accounts a wonderfully agreeable man whose company gave Reed and the rest of them much pleasure. Agramonte, who had been Lazear's classmate in medical school, called him "the type of the old southern gentleman, affectionate with a high sense of honor, a staunch friend and faithful." Lazear had just joined the volunteer Army Medical Corps, having presented recommendations from William Welch himself. He was uneasily aware of being only thirty-three, but his background was formidable, including graduation in medicine from Columbia, an internship at Bellevue, work in pathology and bacteriology in Germany, and a teaching appointment at the Hopkins Hospital, where he worked under Osler and Thayer. As Thayer's junior associate, he had investigated the details of the newly discovered role of the mosquito in transmitting malaria. In his twenty-page report on electrozone, Reed carefully gave Lazear credit for helping him.

In Washington once again, Reed wrote in April to Kean, congratulating him on becoming the chief sanitary officer of Havana. He noted that Sternberg, who was "cross as a bear," had already selected the men (*other* men, of course) to attend the meeting of the Association of Military Surgeons, so neither he nor Kean could plan to go. He also mentioned efforts he was making on behalf of his son, Lawrence, who, after two years in the army, wanted to take the examinations for promotion.

As it happened, Lawrence was involved in events that, although tragicomic in one sense, had tragic and serious implications in another. He was given jury duty at the court martial of an ill-favored perpetual private named Arthur B. Haskins, whose usual unsatisfactory conduct had reached a point that could no longer be tolerated. Haskins was found guilty of bad conduct on June 1, 1900, and was sentenced to hard labor for three months. He was then locked away in the military prison at Piñar del Rio along with seven other soldiers, and Lawrence Reed's duty in that connection was done.

In that prison, away from any source of contamination, Haskins and a man named Schi from Michigan sickened with yellow fever, and Haskins died of it. There had been no visitors to the prison, and no contaminated material had been brought in. The cause of the illness of these two men was altogether mysterious, particularly since the other men and their guards stayed healthy. If something malign—a fungus or a minute and invisible organism, perhaps—were in the air, why had the others not inhaled it, along with the men who sickened? From whatever source Reed heard about this, whether from his son or someone else, the news of yellow fever appearing so inexplicably in a sequestered environment made him sit up, prickling with excited curiosity and surmise. Because the circumstances of the death pointed to a solution of the puzzle, Dr. Philip Hench insisted years later that Haskins should be memorialized. He was a reprobate, but his pain and despair were no less compelling for that reason; and his death made him a key to the solution of an enigma that, unsolved, would continue to bring pain and despair to countless others.

It was just about the time Haskins died that Walter Reed was sent back to Cuba. His orders, which are still on record, commanded him to set up "a board of medical officers . . . to meet at Camp Columbia, Quemados, Cuba, for the purpose of pursuing scientific investigations with reference to the infectious diseases prevalent on the Island of Cuba." Beside Reed, the board was to include James Carroll, Aristides Agramonte, and Jesse Lazear. There was no singling out of yellow fever in the final draft of these orders, but it may be that the first draft indicated it as a target of the investigations proposed. Mrs. Sternberg, writing her husband's biography, declared that yellow fever had been specified at first, and this directive had then been scratched out. Her husband may very well have been hedging. Not only had he come to wonder whether the fever's causative agent would ever be identified, but he was no doubt still smarting from attacks on his corps for its failure to prevent typhoid fever. The letter he wrote as a follow-up to the orders continued the ambiguity, making it appear that Reed was being asked to investigate anything interesting from leprosy to animal diseases. The question of whether or not Sternberg indicated that the focus of Reed's work was to be on yellow fever has been debated by such men as Truby, Kean, and Hench, and the question of whether he gave definite instructions that the board was to investigate the mosquito as vector is even more worrisome. The Reed-Gorgas correspondence, Reed's own letters to Barringer at the University of Virginia, and evidence from Henry Hurd at Hopkins all show that Sternberg felt strongly that the mosquito hypothesis was a waste of time, however much he might insist later, after Reed's triumph, that its study was something he had been hopeful about and indeed had ordered. Leonard Wood is sometimes credited with insisting on the formation of Reed's board, and with setting its goals and defining its mission. An old friend of Reed's, he allocated money for his work at a critical time, making it possible to build Camp Lazear and to pay the volunteer subjects of the experiments.

However eager Reed was to go to Cuba, the cost was, again, severe seasickness. He wrote to his family on June 21, daring at first to boast of an untroubled stomach. But when finally dispatched, the letter was made up of what he called efforts no. one, two, three, and four, for he had been periodically incapacitated by his old enemy. He wrote of sharing a stateroom with Carroll, and reported the presence of several officers on board. Three days later—for he was no man to let grass grow under his feet (or foam pile up) between letters—he wrote of being on

Danger and Disappointment

the mend, thoroughly enjoying the tropical breezes on deck, and the view of the Palm Beach Hotel and the Royal Poinciana through Carroll's opera glasses. He reminisced fondly about their life at Keewaydin, where his family remained, and thought "how dear little daughter would enjoy seeing the schools of flying fish, as they suddenly rise out of the water and go hurrying along." Finally, he was able to write that Morro Castle was in sight and that after reporting to General Wood, he would go at once to Quemados. Except for the perils of seasickness, one might give a wistful backward glance to this kind of travel in view of the current way of making such a trip, enclosed in a throbbing metal bullet for a few empty hours aloft.

Reed no doubt recognized that the lead article on yellow fever and typhoid in the *Army-Navy Journal* for June 23 was a whistle in the dark. It stated that: "The yellow fever outlook in Havana is one to give satisfaction to those who have been administering the affairs of Cuba and comfort to those who have relatives or friends on the island. Havana is now in very good sanitary condition as a whole, with apparently little liability to any epidemic visitation whether of yellow fever or other disease." Reed's letters give the lie to this sanguine view, however, for he wrote: "Fortunately for the purposes of this Board, an epidemic of yellow fever was prevailing in the adjacent town of Quemados, Cuba, at the time of our arrival, thus furnishing us an opportunity for clinical observations and for bacteriological and pathological work."

Quemados was a beautiful tropical village whose pastel houses nestled among the brilliant green hills splashed with the scarlet and purple of hibiscus and bougainvillea. And in the midst of all that loveliness, a man from the Seventh Cavalry, who lived on General Lee Street among other army people and some civilians, fell ill. It turned out that his wife had been sick for some time, bleeding and growing weaker before she would tell the army doctors of her condition because she was terrified at having her sickness named and afraid of the ward where people with such sickness were taken, often to die almost at once.

WALTER REED

Within a few days, a sergeant fell ill, with fever and blinding headache. He was then moved into the infectious ward, and all the inhabitants of no. 20 General Lee Street were quarantined. Then another private became feverish, and within three days the sergeant's daughter was sick. The sergeant himself died on the last day of the month. Jesse Lazear examined his body and confirmed everyone's worst fears.

From this beginning, yellow fever moved rapidly around the pleasant little suburban town, seeming by good fortune to skip some nonimmunes, and then coming back to gather them up in its grim harvest. Since no yellow fever bacterium was known, diagnosis had to be made according to symptoms, and through the process of eliminating other possible causes of all that pain and debilitation. Lazear could only demonstrate that there was no malarial plasmodium in the blood of a victim; he could not point to something he did see and implicate it. Although he was primarily interested in malaria, he caught some mosquitoes—just in case—and put them in glass tubes, taking them to his laboratory for a thorough look through his microscope. Perhaps they did contain something other than the malaria agent. Gorgas, who talked with Lazear, was always convinced that he was "probably the first member of the commission who entertained the idea of the disease being carried by the mosquito." He may have been the first in the commission, but the idea that the mosquito and other insects carry disease was far from new in any company. It was an old notion when Benjamin Rush spoke in 1793 of the vast swarms of mosquitoes to be seen in Philadelphia at a time of an epidemic there; but until Reed disclosed the *mechanism* of transmission, the idea of a connection was only an intuition.

Alexander Stark, another University of Virginia graduate and a sound physician, was also helping fight the fever in Quemados, writing to the adjutant at Columbia Barracks that no source of the cases at no. 22 General Grant Street had been found. Stark had a quaint but pathetically unfounded belief that yellow fever must somehow be the

Danger and Disappointment

toll paid for some kind of reprehensible conduct, and he was baffled to observe that "all the parties [who were sick] seem to possess excellent characters and disclaim any association with persons likely to be infected or have any of them save (a sergeant) visited the City of Havana for a long period." He put considerable faith in burning contaminated property and planned to "destroy all property by fire deemed necessary."

If any proof were needed to show that a clean mind and a clean body did not promote immunity to yellow fever, the illness of Jefferson Kean supplied it. His was the first case Reed ever saw. Kean thought that laundry done "in a multitude of unsanitary places" might spread the disease, and to defend this view he pointed to "the Cuban custom of washing many garments successively in the water so as to save water and soap," and the failure to boil laundry. Then he pondered that bordellos might in some way be responsible, revoking night passes because "the danger [of yellow fever] is greatly increased if the men are permitted to spend the night in these houses." Stark saw danger in a saloon at no. 90 Real Street, situated in a building that let rooms. His misgivings were perhaps more reasonable than Kean's, however, since the saloon was next to no. 20 General Lee Street, where the epidemic first appeared.

Kean had sent his family north just a week before yellow fever broke out in Marianao, "taking a heavy toll of the American population." He saw all the suspicious cases in Marianao and in the vicinity of Columbia Barracks until the headquarters staff ordered him to stop visiting yellow fever victims as long as he was based in the headquarters and messing with the officers. He obeyed this order, but then a question of friendship arose. "Major Edmunds and his wife took the disease and his condition became very alarming. . . . I was too much worried about him to sleep," he wrote later, "and so arose at daybreak on the 16th of June and went over to his house. . . . There I complied with the letter . . . of my order by sitting on the porch and talking through the window, which was closed only with an iron grill." Five days later he was "taken with the usual symptoms of the disease" and sent to the hospital. After recovering, he took leave to recuperate with his family in New Jersey, experiencing "the period of prostration and mental depression which always follows this disease," although his bout with it was considered to have been "of only moderate severity."

If anything had been needed to bring home to the American investigators the gravity of their situation, Kean's illness awoke them to the danger in which all the nonimmune physicians lived. Not only was death always a possibility, but the terrible ethical dilemma of risky experimentation on human subjects had to be faced. Reed had made a will before leaving home, giving everything to Emilie, to whom he explained that a man his age should have a will in any case. His letters home now became almost painfully cheery. He dwelt at length on his discovery of the Latin lateral showerbath, declaring that "we must have a shower at Keewaydin—not one of those overhead affairs, but one that throws the spray in a curve, so that one's head doesn't get wet."

He chattered on as though he were on holiday:

> Yesterday I went down to Havana and ordered *two* suits of *crash* made. They cost $6.00 a suit and are very cool and pretty. The weather here doesn't begin to be as warm as Washington in Summer. The breezes, both day and night, are indescribably delicious. Our mess is very good and the messmates are Dr. and Mrs. Stark, Drs. Lazaer [sic], Porter, Pinto and Carroll, with the funniest looking heathen Chinese cook you ever saw!

He gloated over a windfall of $71.42 that had come his way, apparently indemnity for some unspecified injury to his kneecap. And he gloated too over Lawrence's recent success in his examinations:

> There were 6 candidates, 3 of whom passed. He calls me up on the phone every evening and we have a jolly chat for about 5 minutes. . . . He applied for the artillery and yesterday Gen. Lee told me that Cap't Harmon's endorsement was a very strong one and that he had added another

Danger and Disappointment

strong one to it. . . . Weather here delightful, both day and night. Don't you and little Joy work too hard at the flowers and piano. . . . Oh! for a taste of those strawberries! But I'll have a cold *Mango* for breakfast. Good-bye, you precious hearts.

A letter of the same date to his chief referred, in quite another vein, to the urgency of getting work done on the typhoid study and reported that he had lost no time in Cuba.

> Yesterday we took careful cultures from two cases that have slightly passed the most active stage. Lazear has cultures from three autopsies to be worked up. This afternoon we will take cultures from the blood of a case admitted to camp hospital last evening and will continue to take cultures each successive day. . . . Lazear and I will probably go to Cienfuegos next week to look into an epidemic of malarial fever amongst Second Infantry there.

On the following day he wrote again to Sternberg, asking that Private Augustus Tracy, in whose handling of laboratory animals he had come to have great faith while in the museum, be transferred to work with him in Cuba and that he bring with him a shipment of such animals for use in his Cuban laboratory. "Life is too short," he noted, "to train an ignorant man." He somehow found time that day to write at length to "Cricket . . . My precious little daughter." He told her, "You will never know until you try it, how very delightful it is to just jump out of bed at 5:30 o'clock in the morning and rush in and take a bath! It makes you feel like a young grasshopper just out of the morning dew!" He noted that Lawrence "talks through the telephone real 'biggity,' " and he asked if she were continuing to enjoy her piano and was playing "Ragtime" and "I want you, my honey" and "those other classical tunes."

By July 8 it was no longer possible to avoid referring to yellow fever in his letters home. Emilie had seen an item about it in the *Washington Evening Star,* and forwarded it to her husband, seeking reassurance. Reed had also seen it when a young colleague called it to his attention. His reaction echoed Osler's view that "If you see anything in

WALTER REED

[the newspapers] that you know is true begin to doubt it at once." He explained:

I didn't want to give you any worry, especially as I wasn't myself taking any risks whatever. There have been two or three cases . . . since our arrival . . . one a member of the hospital corps, and another a female nurse, both of whom were nursing Mrs. Edmunds who was down with the disease in an infected house in Quemados. These cases are now convalescing. Dr. Kean is over his attack. . . . Dr. Carroll and I have been studying some cultures . . . from the blood of yellow fever [patients] but there isn't a particle of danger in this. Please don't pay any attention to anything you see in the papers, for they always get everything wrong. I couldn't be in a safer place on the Island than at Camp Columbia. By Genl. Lee's order, all Americans had already moved out of Quemados before we got here. No soldier is allowed to enter the town and no case has occurred for about two weeks. The last . . . was that of a Spanish boy who lived about 2 miles from here. When I get the disease [sic] I promise that a cable gram shall be promptly sent to you. We are not going into infected houses nor to see patients with the disease. We will confine our work to material that Dr. Agramonte brings us. At present, there are about a dozen cases in Havana, but none of them at our disposal. So please rest easy as far as I am concerned.

James Carroll also wrote reassurances to his wife. He does not seem to have been as devoted a family man as Reed, and he was described by Lazear as "not a very entertaining person . . . with a very narrow horizon." His letters tend to evoke an image of a bald-headed, bespectacled man, who had "a light red mustache, projecting ears and a rather dull expression." After pointing out that "as long as Americans live in new buildings as we do they are perfectly safe," he rather grandly added: "Do not let yourself be made miserable by imagination; look five years ahead and you will find that considerable benefit to all of us will follow this trip. Our results will be looked for by scientists all over the world and you ought really to be as proud of the opportunity as I am myself."

Danger and Disappointment

Poor doomed Jesse Lazear, who had earlier settled his family in Cuba but had been obliged to send them home because of the quarantine, also wrote reassuring letters to his pregnant wife and his mother. In one he sounded somewhat exasperated with the continued effort to disprove the *Bacillus icteroides* that was still rippling around the scientific world, though in ever-fading ripples. "The laboratory work goes on but not as satisfactorily as I had hoped. Dr. Reed had been in the old discussion over Sanarelli's bacillus and he still works on that subject. I am not at all interested in it but want to do work which may lead to the discovery of the real organism. However, I am doing as much as I can."

Reed had not been in Cuba long before something occurred that made him furious. Agramonte, who was on the scene, wrote that "Since the later part of June, reports had been coming to headquarters of an extraordinary increase of sickness among the soldiers stationed at Piñar del Rio, the capital of the extreme western province, and very soon the great mortality from so-called 'pernicious malarial fever' attracted the attention of the chief surgeon, Captain A. N. Stark, who, after consulting with Major Reed, ordered me to go there and investigate." A man had died from "pernicious malaria" just the night before Agramonte arrived. He did an autopsy, and declared the cause of death to be yellow fever. . . ." Lieutenant Godfrey and Acting Resident Surgeon Presnell, with Robert Cooke as junior associate, were responsible. "A search through the military hospital wards revealed the existence of several unrecognized cases being treated as malaria; a consultation held with the medical officer in charge showed me his absolute incapacity, as he was under the influence of opium most of the time (he committed suicide several months afterward) and so I telegraphed the condition of things to headquarters." The post commander, refusing to believe the diagnosis, "was loath to abandon his comfortable quarters for the tent life in the woods" and did nothing. Stark, appealed to, sent word at once that Reed would hurry to join Agramonte, that nurses were being sent, and that strict quarantine should be instituted. Reed then reviewed the case histories with Agramonte, much as they had once gone over material together in the medical museum in Washington. Agramonte was thought to have had a mild attack of the disease as a child and to have obtained immunity from it. The two studied sick reports for the two previous months, "fruitlessly trying to place the blame upon the first case." Agramonte wrote later that as they stood in the men's sleeping quarters where there were several beds from which men fatally stricken with yellow fever had been removed, they were "struck by the fact that the later occupants had not developed the disease." Reed wrote the surgeon general about Piñar del Rio on July 24:

> It seems bad enough when medical officers insist upon confounding typhoid fever and malaria, in spite of symptoms, failure of quinine, and . . . distinctive postmortem lesions present in every case, [and] persist in calling yellow fever "pernicious malarial fever." . . . In Cuba in the month of June, it about reaches the sublimest heights of obtuseness! Agramonte . . . autopsied one case, in the presence of these medical officers, and had found marked fatty degeneration of liver and fluid blood in stomach and upper intestine.
>
> Notwithstanding this, Godfrey & A. A. Sug. Presnell . . . had the sublime impudence to tell me that they wished it distinctly understood that they differed with Dr. Agramonte & still considered these cases as pernicious malarial fever! Agramonte and I autopsied the Commissary Sergt. who had died after a 3 days illness. The stomach contained considerable black-vomit material & the liver was typical —body fairly well jaundiced. In the presence of this case, these gentlemen reluctantly yielded. I find that the cases (11 had died) had all presented unmistakable symptoms of yellow fever, except in the matter of albumen in the urine, which test Godfrey had left in the hands of one of his stewards, who was quite incompetent. . . . These cases had been treated on the wards of the hospital like other patients, without any particular disinfection of bed linen & clothing except that on the bed, when the patient died . . .

Danger and Disappointment

sheets and pillow slips went into bichloride and mattrass [sic] was sponged over with bichloride.

The time would come when Reed would find nothing dangerous in such failure to disinfect, but the failure in diagnosis was a different matter. He was wrong when he stated briskly that he felt confident "that by strict quarantine, another week will end the trouble," but when Philip Hench asked Kean more than forty years later about Godfrey's negligence, Kean replied, "I thought at the time that he should have been court martialed and I still think so." Godfrey, who had once attended the University of Virginia but had his medical degree from Maryland, was the son of an infantry major then in Cuba; he was not the only physician there, but the others were contract surgeons, and he was surgeon-in-charge. A blistering letter from Stark was sent to him, as well as to a contract surgeon in charge of the yellow fever ward, Robert Page Cooke. Cooke was without any experience with yellow fever, having just graduated from the University of Virginia. Kean thought his contract should be broken, pointing to his deficiencies in record keeping that added to the difficulty of making accurate diagnosis. But he softened toward the neophyte, whom he came to think of as "always a very modest and manly gentleman," when Cooke—in spite of having been given a job without preparation and appropriate instructions—faced the criticism unflinchingly and offered himself as a volunteer for yellow fever tests.

CHAPTER IX

Some Gains—and
a Bitter Loss

In July of 1900 Walter Reed wrote home about a visit from two English physicians sent out by the School of Tropical Medicine at Liverpool to study yellow fever. Drs. Durham and Myers were so well trained and so eager that he may have worried that they would publish findings from Havana before his board could make its own report. Nonetheless, they were welcome guests, and the need to offer them hospitality made for some splendid occasions, which Reed took pleasure in describing in great detail in his letters home.

He told of a breakfast party for the Englishmen, saying that he and Mrs. Stark had planned the meal, which included "A horn of 1841 Brandy with Soda—Soup a la China—Red Snapper with sauce inimitable—Saratoga potatoes—Old Scotch whiskey served in glasses stolen from the Governor General's palace—Potato salad—

Scotch whisky with cracked ice & Belfast ginger ale—Black coffee—followed by old Scotch plain & undiluted." He went on to tell about Ramon, "the small Jap boy, with a helmet that some soldier has given him perched on his head, hind part before, . . . who calls me his friend and pats me on the back very affectionately." The only worry he let creep into his letter is one about the Boxer Rebellion in China. "We hear . . . that the legations are all safe —What glorious news after the dreadful suspense of the last 3 weeks. We can only hope that it is true; still one cannot believe anything he sees in the news papers." And he wrote of his anticipation of returning home "to see his sweet girls once more, and to taste some of those good vegetables," adding that his stay in Cuba had been "so much more pleasant than . . . anticipated."

It is pleasant to think of the convivial breakfast with the English visitors, since it was a reprieve from the considerable anxiety and grief that were so soon to follow. The guests of honor went on to South America, where both contracted yellow fever and Myers died of it. The report Durham published on the yellow fever expedition in 1902 expressed warm thanks to the members of the Reed board and credited that board with many of its findings.

The cleaning and fumigating with which the Americans thought to quell yellow fever were not effective. Cubans watched with amusement as the loco Norte Americanos toiled away—and continued dying of the disease. Gorgas reported that "the squads searched out every back street, every blind alley, every hut . . . the severest quarantine measures were applied to all incoming ships; yellow fever patients were isolated in a secluded hospital," but "the only response was a steady increase in the disease."

The city's military governor, Gen. William Ludlow, died of it. The chief commissary officer, Major Patterson, got it. A cable was sent to his wife in Cincinnati with the news, but by the time she arrived in Cuba her husband was dying. "When she realized that death was approaching, her grief was pathetic. To the horror of those who witnessed the scene, Mrs. P., crazed with sorrow, threw herself upon her husband, thus covering herself with *vomito negro,* the gruesome accompaniment of death from yellow fever. Clasping her husband in her arms, she begged him to ask God to take her, too, and soon. Conscious to the very end, he prayed for this." Mrs. Patterson shot herself when their prayer went unanswered, and husband and wife were buried together on the following day in Camp Columbia's growing military cemetery.

A member of the commanding general's staff who attended the Pattersons' funeral found himself shivering as the coffins went into the ground, and within forty-eight hours he too was dead. Two days after having a chill, the American superintendent of the San Jose Asylum died. A mess of eight men, organized by the chief quartermaster, Chauncey B. Baker, had begun using at meals the old English toast (to be revived in World War II)—"To those who are gone already and here's to the next to go!" Before long, only Baker and the general's aide-de-camp, a man named Brooks, were left. Baker recalled later that Brooks lifted his glass to him, whereupon he said, "Brooks, I won't drink that toast to myself. You had yellow fever in Santiago . . . and won't have it again. Besides that, you are a teetotaler. . . . So I'll drink my wine but not the toast." Baker escaped the fever, as it happened, but morale everywhere was low. From June 1 through October 19, 1900, there were 789 *reported* cases of yellow fever in the furiously sanitized city of Havana.

The surgeon general's report devoted pages to ways of treating yellow fever—some were disputed, some recommended; some innocuous, some drastic. One called for the ingestion of salol, a phenol derivative said to calm irritation of the stomach and bowels and thereby to reduce the temperature. Gorgas and other critics pointed out that this rather insoluble substance was turned by pancreatic juice into "salicylic acid 60, carbolic acid 40, a combination more suitable for cleaning floors." It clearly had dire side effects, including "intense headache, profuse sweat, delirium, and even "frequent epileptiform convulsions." Those ordered to administer salol greatly favored milder measures such as sponge baths, lemonade, and mustard footbaths. Gorgas, who pointed out that he had seen nearly every case of yellow fever in Havana in the past year and had been familiar with the treatment in each case, did "not believe that any particular medicine should be urged for any particular symptom," charging American (and many Cuban) physicians with dosing too much in any case.

Such a time of anxious bafflement and danger was a pressure cooker that exacerbated the differences among the men engaged in such unpleasant work so far from home. Truby and Hench, writing separately about the life in Havana in 1900, have been able to flesh out for us some of the characters in this drama. For example, a man who was to volunteer for the experiments yet to come, Alva Sherman Pinto, held that Agramonte was "about the lamest excuse of a doctor I ever associated with. . . . He just bluffed his way through." It was true that Agramonte's first qualification for the board had been his immunity to yellow fever, assumed on the basis of a mild attack in childhood, which enabled him to conduct autopsies. Kean preferred Carroll, whom he found straightforward and reliable, although he had done a number of "improper things"; he indicated that although Reed might not have given Carroll credit for all he did, it was Reed who had elevated him to a position of importance.

Robert Cooke, whose trial by fire must have made him exquisitely sensitive to differences in the pecking order, wrote about Agramonte in 1900 that he was

> . . . a Cuban gentleman of the highest type . . . somewhat above average height and weight, a rather large head, fine brow, . . . a small moustache . . . very genial and a clever conversationalist. His professional attainments were of a high order. . . . His qualifications as a pathologist and diagnostician in doubtful cases were most helpful to Major Reed who had the utmost confidence in his judgement. Agramonte was entrusted with all the autopsy work—a

Some Gains—and a Bitter Loss

very important phase in the task of throwing light into the
dark places of this mysterious malady.

Agramonte himself felt sufficiently slighted by history to
produce his personal and slanted version of those days
under the somewhat florid title of "The Inside History of a
Great Medical Discovery," which appeared in the *Scientific
Monthly* for December 1915. In this he speaks of Walter
Reed as "a bacteriologist of some repute," and a man who
"deservedly enjoyed the full confidence of the Surgeon
General, besides his personal friendship and regard." He
saw Reed as "a man of charming personality, honest and
above board," someone everyone loved and confided in, "a
polished gentleman and a scientist of the highest order."
Retrospective opinion about James Carroll ranges from
Cooke's view of him as "a self-made man . . . risen from
the ranks through his own efforts" to Pinto's blunt recol-
lection of him as "reticent," rather surly, and ill-educated.
Pinto took the occasion to say that "sometimes, if a man
keeps his mouth shut people think he's smart. He [Carroll]
would talk when talked to, but he didn't volunteer much
information."
A letter Carroll wrote his wife on the day in August
when he had been given the virus of yellow fever by a
mosquito bite, indicates a rather peevish man whose basic
self-distrust evokes a certain sympathy. Apparently his
wife had forwarded an appeal from one "Hattie," who
should be told that he was "not in a position to help." He
added that "if I were able I should hesitate a long while on
account of the impertinence, vulgarity and selfishness
shown. I am however not yet able to support my wife and
children who do not treat me that way." He went on to
thank his wife for sending him peaches, but took pains to
point out that not only were the express charges likely to
be exorbitant but the peaches were likely to have spoiled
en route; and that she might hope for no more than $100
a month from him.
Then, fumblingly and grudgingly, he let his heart show

for a moment with the rather acute observation that although she complained of their little son's lack of affection for her, she "must not expect a man or a boy to be like a girl. . . . I know Jamie likes to be petted and when he pushes you away it is not because he does not like it but because he does." In closing his letter he asks her to pray "for all you are worth."

Another letter from that time and place is poignant for another reason. It was written by Jesse Lazear, the serious young physician who was, Pinto said, "a gentleman to everyone," and who liked Havana because there he was not expected to play golf. It went to his mother, and was among the last he ever wrote. It speaks of his happiness over the news of the birth of his daughter and of his anticipation of a trip home in October. It ends, "I have a good deal of driving around over rough roads just now and I am usually pretty tired in the evening."

In early August Walter Reed was summoned back to Washington to help get out the typhoid report. After the death of Shakespeare in June, work on it was stalled, and Sternberg wanted Reed and Vaughan to complete it. While preparing to embark on the journey home, Reed found that zealous port officials wanted to autoclave everything in sight. He wrote later:

> I packed my trunk . . . and took it to Havana, in order to have it and its contents thoroughly disinfected preparatory to boarding the transport, Rawlins, on Wednesday. You never saw anything like the care with which every piece of wearing apparel is subjected to steam or formalin, for fear that yellow jack may be conveyed to the United States. Of course, it was absurd to disinfect my baggage, but no exceptions are made. Wednesday morning the contents of my valise will also be put in the big sterilizer.

Faced with his usual problem at sea, he christened the ship the "Rollin's"; when it reached the States, he was hurried away without benefit of the normal quarantine. Truby, who had accompanied him, noted that a quarantine launch came out after hours especially for Reed, probably at the request of the surgeon general.

Some Gains—and a Bitter Loss

Although Reed was reunited for a while with the distaff side of his family, he had left his son in Cuba and must have felt some anxiety about him. In August Lawrence got his commission at last, and wrote his family that since becoming officer of the day, "*Of course* I have been dignified to beat the band. I guess that's the reason I have had a headache." He reported being "on top of the world" with a congenial regimental mess, in a lovely place where there was swimming, living "far better than most families do in Cuba and very inexpensive."

Lazear and Carroll continued to work with Agramonte in Cuba. On August 19 the board, with the exception of Agramonte, who was already acquainted with his work, went to call on Finlay, who must have been elated at this long-delayed recognition of twenty years of work on yellow fever—for which he held the female of what is now called *Aedes aegypti* (a common house mosquito) accountable. Finlay showed his visitors a cluster of tiny cigar-shaped mosquito eggs in a bowl with some water in the bottom. The eggs clung to the bowl's sides, slightly out of water, and had begun to dry. Finlay had found that such eggs could be dried, frozen, or blown around for up to three months and still hatch into larvae at the first warm rain. Within three days, once they were moistened and warmed, they would become larvae, and after a week more, pupae. Then, in a few days' time, mosquitoes would emerge. Reed and Carroll had spent considerable time back in Washington at the Bureau of Entomology studying this very mosquito, learning to differentiate it from others that might be found in Havana.

Finlay had been studying the possibility of the mosquito's being implicated in yellow fever for much of his adult life, feeling sure of what was happening in general without being able to prove how. Did the female, the only one that bites for a blood meal, insert eggs into her victim, or deposit some poison? Did she pass infection on to her offspring, as ticks do, so a new generation could convey the disease to its victims? Did she infect by means of her dirty needlelike bill, as an infected hypodermic needle conveys hepatitis? Or was Manson right in thinking that the poison it had taken in made the insect sick so that it fell into water that in turn poisoned people who drank it?

The tenacious Henry Rose Carter had sent a memorandum to Lazear about Finlay's mosquitoes, noting that "the a priori argument for Dr. F's theory has much in its favor." Yet Carter did not find Finlay's observations convincing; they seemed to him "scarcely corroborative," and he sent along a pamphlet about his own work concerning the "interval required from the development of the infecting case until the environment is capable of developing infection among other men"—the period needed for extrinsic incubation. What happened, he asked, to "the material leaving the person of the patient" that made it infect someone else? "It may be a change in the physical state of the excretion infecting the environment, as when the sputum of tuberculosis must become dry and pulverelent [sic] before it produces infection," or "it may be transmitted only by a 'host.'" He surmised that "the specific microorganism when it left the person of the patient, was incapable of producing infection in man," but that "under proper conditions" it could so change as to be able to do so. "For this," he said, "I know of no analogy in any other pathogenic microorganisms." It was well known that only the female mosquito needs blood, and she bites only when she needs a blood meal for her eggs to be fertile.

When Finlay's eggs hatched, some of the insects were shipped to Howard for identification. All the other females were kept, each in a glass tube stopped with cotton. Lazear took good care of them, and some were permitted to bite patients with yellow fever being cared for in Las Animas Hospital.

The need for experimentation on humans had become clear. On August 1, before leaving for the States, Reed had written that "There is plenty of material in Havana, with every probability for its rapid increase. . . . Personally, I feel that only can experimentation on human beings serve to clear the field for further effective work.

Some Gains—and a Bitter Loss

With one or two points cleared up, we could then work to so much better advantage." And Carroll noted that it was agreed among the members of the board that they "would themselves be bitten and subject themselves to the same risk that necessity compelled them to impose on others."

When neither Lazear nor Pinto got yellow fever after being bitten on August 11 by mosquitoes that had bitten yellow fever patients, consternation was more marked than relief. The crestfallen Finlay thought something must have been wrong in the technique used, and he was right; the failure of these and seven other "inoculations" was explained when the Reed board found out "that patients after the third day of the disease cannot convey the infection to the mosquito and . . . that after having bit a yellow fever case the mosquito cannot transmit the disease until after an interval of at least twelve days." In short, extrinsic incubation was the key!

On August 27, Lazear spent the entire morning at the hospital coaxing his "bird" to light on and take blood from yellow fever patients. His method was to invert a test tube containing a mosquito so that the insect would fly up into the glass enclosure; he would then remove the cotton stopper and would quickly place the open end of the tube on a forearm or stomach of a willing donor. After a moment or two the insect would light and bite. After it had become engorged, Lazear would disturb it gently by tapping on the sides of its glass prison and would get it to fly up and into the tube so he could imprison it again. It was tedious work, even for a bacteriologist, and had to be done with delicacy and care. On the twenty-seventh there was one reluctant mosquito that had not bitten, but as noon approached Lazear gathered her up with all the rest of his little "birds" and took her back to Camp Columbia. He was beginning to lose respect for the insects as carriers, but was enough of a scientist to continue the meticulous care and feeding of his laboratory charges. Carroll and Lazear were more concerned with the insect's survival than with any possible risk. Agramonte was to recall:

This mosquito had been hatched in the laboratory and in due time fed upon yellow fever blood from a severe case on August 15, that is, twelve days before, the patient then being in the second day of his illness; also at three other times, six days, four days and two days before. Of course, at the time, no particular attention had been drawn to this insect, except that it refused to suck blood when tempted that morning.

After luncheon that day, as Carroll and Lazear were in the laboratory attending to their respective work, the conversation turning upon the mosquitoes and their apparent harmlessness, Lazear remarked how one of them had failed to take blood, at which Carroll thought that he might try to feed it as otherwise it was liable to die before the next day (the insect seemed weak and tired); the tube was carefully held first by Lazear and then by Carroll himself, for a considerable length of time, upon his forearm before the mosquito decided to introduce its proboscis.

A couple of days later, while they were swimming late in the afternoon, Carroll had a terrible headache, and Pinto, looking at him, declared he must have yellow fever. Although Carroll retorted, "Don't be a damned fool—I have no such thing," he was tucked away in the yellow fever ward by 8 P.M., much to his chagrin. Pinto noted that he was obstinate and had to be ordered to the hospital, but he soon became delirious and was very ill. His physician companions said he was "in bad shape for more than a week." This was an understatement; he nearly died. On the day Carroll sickened, the thirtieth, Lazear applied the same mosquito that had bitten him and three other persons to another healthy volunteer. And this man came down with "a mild but well marked case" of yellow fever. So it was clear that the mosquito that had bitten James Carroll had been ripe and ready.

Having succeeded, Agramonte and Lazear were horrified. They did not want to believe what had happened. Carroll was so sick and went down so fast that his friends were in a turmoil. They had half persuaded themselves that the mosquito was fairly harmless, that Reed had kept them going on a futile chase. They frantically "searched for all possibilities that might throw the blame for his infection upon any other source than the mosquito which bit him four days before." But when they found such a possibility in Carroll's reluctant acknowledgment of having unwisely gone into the yellow fever wards, the autopsy rooms, and into Havana too during the interval implicated, it only made matters worse, and placed them in an agonizing can't-win situation. They were sure he had sickened from the bite of their experimental mosquito, but they could reap no benefit from his illness in the way of experimental proof because there remained an outside chance that he had been infected by another mosquito elsewhere or by something else. In the meantime, they were desperately anxious that he not die. Lazear exhibited more heart than logic when he tried to console himself by recalling that Carroll had offered himself to the mosquito and had himself held its tube to his arm until it drew blood.

It was clear that they would have to get the mosquitoes to bite other volunteers under controlled circumstances. According to Agramonte's report, they

> . . . decided to test it upon the first non-immune person who should offer himself to be bitten; this was . . . taken much as a joke among the soldiers about the military hospital. Barely fifteen minutes may have elapsed since we had come to this decision when, as Lazear stood at the door of the laboratory trying to "coax" a mosquito to pass from one test-tube to another, a soldier came walking by . . . he saluted . . . but, as Lazear had both hands engaged, he answered a rather pleasant "Good morning." The man stopped . . . curious no doubt to see the performance with the tubes . . . and said: "You still fooling with mosquitoes, Doctor?" "Yes," returned Lazear, "will you take a bite?" "Sure, I ain't scared of 'em," responded the man.

Agramonte noted that his name was William E. Dean and that he was a member of Troop B, Seventh Cavalry. "He said that he had never been in the tropics before and had not left the military reservation for nearly two months.

The conditions for a test case were quite ideal." Agramonte confessed to "great trepidation at the time." It was justified, for Dean's was "the first indubitable case of yellow fever about to be produced experimentally by the bite of purposely infected mosquitoes." When Private Dean fell ill according to plan, Agramonte confessed to being, with Lazear, "well-nigh on the verge of distraction." Reed was still away, and Carroll's condition was alarming; he was wracked by the wildest delirium, fighting for his life.

Lazear wrote unhappily about him to Reed on September 2. Gorgas visited him, and was "shocked" at the appearance of the man, who "was lying in a state of prostration, his face flushed with a high fever, his eyes bloodshot, his restless body tossing on the bed." Carroll then lapsed into delirium and in his lucid moments tried to explain that "he had subjected his arm to the bite of an infected mosquito." Gorgas, who refused to accept the mosquito-vector hypothesis until long after Reed had proved it, must have thought Carroll was raving. His nurse certainly thought his babbling about being sick because of a mosquito came from delirium, and so indicated in his record.

Reed was quick to write to Kean of his anxiety about what was going on in his absence:

> I have just seen your last Cablegram dated Sept. 5, giving Carroll's condition. I cannot begin to describe my mental distress and depression over this most unfortunate turn of affairs. I have his letter of August 28th, in which he tells of a trip to the autopsy room of Mil. Hosp. No. 1 and the nasty condition of the interior, stating that he had declined to do any autopsies there until it was thoroughly disinfected. That must have afforded a possible chance for infection.

In referring to the bite Carroll had taken on the twenty-seventh—and which surely had given him his sickness, although scientific proof could not be claimed for it in view of the other exposures—Reed noted sturdily, "We had all determined to experiment on ourselves and I should have taken the same dose had I been there," and repeated his warning that all he had said in the letter was confidential.

By September 7 he was able to relay to Carroll's wife the word from Kean that her husband was "better, but not out of danger." He then wrote to Carroll a solicitous message that was interrupted by the arrival of more good news about his condition. Reed's reply to this was added to Carroll's letter.

> Hip! Hip! Hurrah! God be praised for the news from Cuba today—"Carroll much improved—prognosis very good!" *I* shall simply go out and get BOILING DRUNK! Really I can never recall such a sense of relief in all my life, as the news of your recovery gives me! And . . . would you believe it? The Typhoid Report is on its way to the upper office. . . . I'm damned if I don't get drunk TWICE!!! Come home as soon as you can and see your wife and babies.

On the back of the envelope Reed asked, "Did the *Mosquito DO IT?*"

On September 23 Carroll was able to write his wife that "everybody is surprised at the manner in which I am picking up flesh and strength and all those yellow fever experts remarked how strong I was upon my legs. Yellow fever has no terrors for me now, because I am immune and cannot contract it again, which gives me a great feeling of comfort." Dean also recovered well. But just as it teased the inhabitants of Cuban villages—seeming to withhold its blow when just about to strike another—yellow fever was holding in store for the board a really bitter blow just as spirits rose. On September 18 Jesse Lazear felt out of sorts, and on September 25 he died after a week of agony and delirium so frantic that he had to be restrained. The circumstances in which he contracted the disease were ambiguous.

His colleagues questioned him while he was still coherent, but did not learn much. Agramonte summed up their puzzlement.

WALTER REED

After the case of Dean so plainly demonstrated the certainty of mosquito infection, we had agreed not to tempt fate by trying any more upon ourselves, and even I determined that no mosquito would bite me if I could prevent it, since the subject of my immunity was one that could not be sustained on scientific grounds; at the same time, we felt that we had been called upon to accomplish such work as did not justify our taking risks which then seemed really unnecessary. This we impressed upon Major Reed when he joined us in October and for this reason he was never bitten by infected mosquitoes.

Lazear told us, however, that while at "Las Animas" Hospital the previous Thursday, . . . as he was holding a test-tube with a mosquito upon a man's abdomen, some other insect . . . flying about the room rested upon his hand; at first, he said, he was tempted to frighten it away, but, as it had settled before he had time to notice it, he decided to let it fill and then capture it; besides, he did not want to move in fear of disturbing the insect contained in his tube, which was feeding voraciously. Before Lazear could prevent it, the mosquito that bit him on the hand had flown away. He told us in his lucid moments that, although Carroll's and Dean's cases had convinced him of the mosquito's role in transmitting yellow fever, the fact that no infection had resulted from his own inoculation the month before had led him to believe himself, to a certain extent, immune.

Carroll's account is essentially in agreement.

Dr. Lazear was applying a mosquito . . . to patients in the yellow fever hospital . . . and while [he was] thus engaged a mosquito alighted upon his hand. He allowed it to take its fill, and concluded it was one of the common culex [malaria] mosquitoes which were present in the hospital in large numbers. So little importance did he attach to the incident, that he made no note of it, and related the circumstances to me when he was first taken sick, five days afterward. A week from that date he died.

Walter Reed must have been terribly disturbed by the irony of the situation: Two of the members of the very

Some Gains—and a Bitter Loss

board recently convened to put an end to unscientific conjecture had been random victims. Lazear died and Carroll very nearly died proving nothing, since neither had contracted the fever under controlled circumstances. Anyone contesting the mosquito hypothesis could use Lazear's martyrdom as an example of almost any method of infection. Furthermore, there was need for discretion, even for secrecy.

The camp's commanding officer, Colonel Baldwin of the Seventh Cavalry, had to be kept in the dark lest he stop any test—if he knew what a test was. He was the kind of scientifically illiterate curmudgeon to be found among the army brass of that day. According to Kean, who detested him, "He was a very mean man." The men hated him, and Kean claimed that "he would deny people things" from spite. It was clearly necessary to keep him unaware of what was going on under his very nose, and this could not have been easy.

The day before Lazear died, Reed wrote to Carroll in anguish over the lack of constraint in the experimentation:

> Your letter of Sept. 20th has just been received, telling me of Lazear's attack. . . . Dear Me! I think I have experienced more mental distress during this month . . . than ever before and I had hoped to be happiest during this time. Although Kean's Cable . . . said, "Severe case —much albumen—high temperature," I can but believe that Lazear will pull through. I hope and pray that he does come out alright.
>
> . . . I . . . cannot say that any of your cases, except perhaps Dean's *prove* anything. If you, my dear Doctor, had, prior to your bite remained at Camp Columbia for ten days, then we would have a *clear* case, *but you didn't!* You went just where you might have contracted the disease from another source and unfortunately Lazear was bitten at Los Animas [*sic*] Hospital! *That* knocks his case out; I mean as a thoroughly scientific experiment. . . . If Dean *DID NOT leave the Post after leaving the hospital* his case is *SATISFACTORY* and proves a *great deal*. If his case will withstand criticism, then your and Lazear's . . . would be

confirmatory . . . I firmly believe in the Mosquito theory
and that the mosquito is a very common culex found all
along our seaboard. I am only regretting that two such
valuable lives have been put in jeopardy, under circumstances in which the *results* . . . would not be above criticism.

On the following day, still unaware of Lazear's death, he
wrote Kean, "I somehow feel that Lazear will pull
through, as he is such a good, brave fellow. I have been so
ashamed of myself for being here in a safe country, while
my associates have been coming down with Yellow Jack."
Sternberg had suggested that he not return to Cuba, but
Reed felt "that, as the Senior Member of a Board investi-
gating Yellow Fever, my place is in Cuba, as long as the
work goes on." He did say that he would "take every
precaution" upon his arrival and would not "with the facts
that we now have, allow a 'loaded' mosquito to bite. . . ." He
then took a serious look at where things stood:

> [I] have said that *human* experimentation *alone* could
> determine the question. Just how far Carroll's and Lazear's
> cases go to support that supposition, I don't know. But
> hope to find out when I get there. Personally, I think that
> we are on the eve of an important find and hence am
> writing all of this to you in strictest confidence. Perhaps I
> owe my life to my departure from Cuba, for I had agreed
> to be bitten along with the others. Being an old man, I
> might have been quickly carried off. I only wish Dr. Pinto
> might have had a *mild* attack! Do pray. Don't talk to anyone
> about this line of work of our Board . . . as we shall hope
> soon to publish a preliminary note on the etiology of
> yellow fever.

On the day of Lazear's death, Sternberg sent a cable to
Kean asking him to secure Lazear's notes about the
experiments.

The first word Lazear's young wife had of her husband's
fate came in a brief wire from Kean, who thought that she
had been notified of her husband's illness before he told
her he was dead. The adjutant thought he should be
buried quietly, but Truby insisted on full military honors,

Some Gains—and a Bitter Loss

and he was laid to rest before a gathering of about fifty mourners in the post cemetery—temporarily, as it turned out, for his body was later taken to Baltimore.

He had always been a meticulous scientist, disciplined to keep records of his work in detail. He had noted the history of each mosquito from the time the egg was acquired until it was carefully hatched; the name of the person it bit, and the date; the day of disease onset; and the particulars of its course. Each insect had been isolated in a test tube sealed with cotton, and allowed to feed only when and where Lazear chose. But there was no record left of the mosquito that had bitten him.

Generals Wood and Sternberg, along with the rest of Lazear's colleagues, were convinced that he had put a mosquito to his arm and allowed it to bite him. Some said that he had been uncertain, in the dim light filtering through the foliage outside the window, as to what kind of insect bit him. Perhaps he had overestimated his resistance or his power of recovery, as young healthy men are apt to do. It was widely believed that he had no insurance and had left without support a wife, a son, and a baby daughter he never saw.

Reed hurried back to Cuba, but before he arrived, James Carroll, recovering but apparently not without emotional damage from his bout with the fever, wrote to his wife in a vein that augured ill for the hitherto mutually supportive Reed-Carroll relationship:

> I have [been] . . . looking over Lazear's papers for notes pertaining to our work. There was quite a notice in this morning's papers about Dr. Lazear and your husband is mentioned too. . . . I attended dear Lazear's funeral yesterday. . . . Kean asked me to have everything in the laboratory disinfected, so it would be safe for Dr. Reed to come and work in.
>
> A mosquito nearly killed me and another killed poor Lazear; the same one, that bit me, was allowed to bite another man and he had a mild attack of yellow fever. This is the most important part of our work and Dr. Reed tells me, that we must publish a small paper. . . . Do not men-

tion this to anyone for anything just yet, because it is one of
the discoveries of the century.

Immediately after Reed arrived, Carroll wrote that Colonel Baldwin, asking when he was expected, had said
jokingly, "I think I shall have to accuse him of running
away."

> I thought to myself [Carroll told Jennie] you have no
> idea how nearly you have come to the truth. . . . My friend
> will be as brave as a lion now that the yellow fever season is
> about over and he will take particular care not to take the
> same chances I did. I wish this thing had occurred a month
> later, after election was over. Perhaps then I should have
> stood a better chance for recognition. But I will never get it
> so long as it is in my friends' [sic] power to prevent it. . . .

While still on shipboard, Reed wrote home that Kean
had said Carroll was strong enough to meet him with "our
private conveyance," and that he had decided not to give
him leave, but to go full steam ahead on the completion of
their common work in Cuba, with the goal of being back in
Washington by mid-December to resume teaching at Columbian College "and earn a part of our salaries."

But things did not work out quite that way. When Reed
began his effort to complete the board's preliminary
report, he found he had little to go on and precious little
help. Carroll went home on sick leave. Agramonte was on
leave in the States. Lazear was dead. Reed obtained
Lazear's notebook, which provided the essential clues to
the proof he was after, for when he broke the code, it
became evident that a mosquito could become infected
only by blood taken during the first two or three days of a
person's sickness, before jaundice set in, and that it had to
incubate the virus for at least twelve days to be infectious.

Truby found Reed's "whirlwind of activity" a startling
contrast to his customary "slow and deliberate" method.
He worked far into the night, scratching out and rewrit-
ing, spreading his draft on an oaken mess table with his
source material piled up at one end. A clerk typed the
results, and Reed read drafts to his colleagues, inviting

their criticism—of which very little, if any, was forthcoming. But Reed knew how quickly his report would be attacked when it was realized that it was based on three cases, two of which were uncontrolled. The report did have enough conviction for Kean, who sent out a warning against allowing mosquitoes to breed. Reed sent a cable to Washington in hopes of getting permission to report to the Indianapolis meeting of the American Public Health Association, and told his wife to expect him by October 18.

It was not like him to be so hasty. He worried that Durham and Myers might beat him into print with his own favorite hypothesis, but no doubt he also felt the urgency of saving as many people from yellow fever as possible. That September was the worst month for the disease in Havana in two years; the hospitals admitted 269 cases in September alone, and the death rate was 20 percent. With Kean, he went to call on General Wood the day before sailing for the States. According to Kean, Reed, "tall, slender, keen and emotional," described his experiments "with that earnest and persuasive eloquence of which he was a master." The military governor responded at once with an offer of $10,000 for his work, adding, "If that is not enough, I will give you $10,000 more."

Camp Lazear was assured.

CHAPTER X

Vindicated

R eed's name was not among those on the printed program of the American Public Health Association when it met in Indianapolis on October 23, 1900, but Sternberg had had a place made for him because of the timeliness of new information about yellow fever. Addressing the 150 delegates in the elaborately decorated hall, Reed used up the twenty minutes he was allowed and was granted another twenty. He was met with indifference.

The press was equally indifferent, the *Indianapolis News* limiting its coverage to little more than a statement that "Surgeon Reid [sic] had presented a paper, 'Some Observations on the Yellow Fever in Cuba.'" Fortunately, Reed did run into some old friends, including Abbott from the Hopkins Hospital, and there are accounts of considerable conviviality among them. But he soon began to worry about having left a draft of his presentation with Sternberg, one that he now realized contained some ambiguities and oversights. After writing Sternberg about a few emendations he considered necessary, he was upset rather than pleased to learn that his chief had already released his report for publication to the *Philadelphia Medical Journal,* one of the country's leading medical communications. He did not even have a chance to review galley proofs. Carroll, Agramonte, and Lazear were named as contributing authors to "The Etiology of Yellow Fever: A Preliminary Note, by Walter Reed, M.D."; and a number of workers in the field, including Carter, Finlay, and Howard, the entomologist, were given credit in the text, which discussed the illness of Carroll and Lazear at length.

Reed had written: "Since we here, for the first time record a case in which a typical attack of yellow fever has followed the bite of an infected mosquito, within the usual period of incubation of the disease, and in which other sources of infection can be excluded, we feel confident that the publication of these observations must excite renewed interest in the mosquito theory of the propagation of yellow fever, as first proposed by Finlay." He then concluded that the Sanarelli Bacillus icteroides *"stands in no causative relation to yellow fever, but, when present, should be considered as a secondary invader"* and that *"the mosquito serves as the intermediate host for the parasite of yellow fever."*

The article attracted somewhat more attention in print than had the presention by its author. The *Washington Post* heaped scorn on "the mosquito hypothesis," calling it "the silliest beyond compare" and scorning the men on the board with the phrase "whoever they may be."

Reed may have been grateful for his escape to Cuba on November 5. Although seasick en route, he wrote home, turning over in his mind happy memories of his family —the "two precious girls and how sweet [they were] to Papa while he was in Washington. And how sweet they were to each other, too." He had sent them candy from New York. He was enjoying "the quiet beauty of the Florida coast" and the hopeful contemplation of the defeat of "that big-mouth Bryan" in the pending election.

Vindicated

Once again in Havana, he lost no time in consulting with General Wood about the work ahead of him. On November 9 he wrote of having located an isolated site about two miles from Quemados for the observation camp, Camp Lazear, which was to be in the charge of Dr. Ames. He warned that "Whether we will be able to carry out further observations will depend upon our ability to get immigrants . . . willing to undertake the risk of being bitten." He assured his wife that he would devote his time to laboratory work and study of stained sections of the mosquito "for the discovery, if possible, of the parasite," and that she had no reason to worry about him.

Within a few days he was able to write Sternberg that three candidates for "the mosquito inoculation had offered themselves" and that he anticipated no problem in getting subjects for the experiment with presumably infected bedding (fomites). The weather was surprisingly chilly, and this was altering the number of yellow fever cases in a way favorable to the population but disadvantageous to the investigators. He noted that Carroll had returned from the States. Sternberg's reply expressed gratification over the progress being made, particularly since he felt strongly that "The profession generally will not be disposed to accept the experiments already published as definitely settling the question as to the role of the mosquito."

Sternberg's expectation was correct. Eugene Wasdin made a statement in the *Philadelphia Medical Journal* pointing with utter scorn to "the inutility of the method employed" by the Reed board, and claiming that it was so inappropriate as to make their claim of the absence of Sanarelli's Bacillus icteroides in the blood of yellow fever victims beneath notice. Wasdin insisted that "nothing has been proved" and "Pure speculation cannot be accepted." The appearance of this article in the same distinguished journal that had published Reed's report was a serious professional insult.

His morale must have been further reduced by the news that Carroll had received a grieving letter from Lazear's widow. She thanked him for his letter of condolence and for attending to some business affairs on her behalf. Regretting that she had to "ask such a favor of a stranger," she besought him for the particulars of her husband's death. A letter from General Wood indicating that her husband had permitted a mosquito to bite him had horrified her. "Much as I know Dr. Lazear loved his work," she wrote, "I can hardly think he could have allowed his enthusiasm to carry him so far." She asked, "Did he feel positive he would get well if he took the fever and did he know that he could not get well as soon as you did?" She longed to believe it was all a dreadful accident.

Since the spring of 1900, Reed had been exchanging letters with Leland Howard, the American authority on insects, and more and more he reached out for his help. Howard was delighted to assist Reed and his colleagues to a better acquaintance with *A. aegypti*—provided they would send him insects to add to his collection. Having located, as he thought, the characteristic markings of a lyre on *Culex fasciatus* (the earlier designation for *A. aegypti*), Reed sought confirmation from Howard. Fearful lest the small supply of eggs Finlay had donated prove inadequate for all he wanted to do, he went deeper and deeper into the study of entomology while his comrades played euchre and poker and passed the time talking of things of general interest. He had a packing box full of books and pamphlets on the subject, and sometimes persuaded his comrades to listen to some of the fine points. Truby remembered that "Soon he had us collecting mosquitoes with a large-mouthed cyanide bottle. These specimens we would study with strong hand lenses. . . . When one was found which we could not identify, off it would go by mail to Howard in Washington."

There was indeed a great deal to learn. *Aedes aegypti* is a vulnerable insect, all gossamer wing, with fragile legs and slim, frangible antennae. Incapable of long flight, she can nonetheless move with great agility at 600 wingbeats a second. She likes human dwellings, and can hover until

Vindicated

the sensors in her legs and antennae encourage her to alight. Apparently the carbon dioxide exuded by humans attracts her, although she seems to respond in a choosy, idiosyncratic way. She does not stab her victim, but delicately inserts her proboscis, which is much finer than a human hair. The insertion might not be noticed if she did not drool a tiny amount of anticoagulant into the wound; it is this that causes itching. After sucking blood, she lays her eggs, seeking a moist spot for this purpose. Her eggs can survive for as long as five years and still mature, given the right conditions. Her male counterpart offers no offense to man.

Millions of dollars and lakes of insecticides have been spent in efforts to annihilate them, and they were once almost totally eliminated from the coastal cities of the Western Hemisphere where yellow fever was a problem. Still, even in the United States they persist, in a zone that reaches from Florida across the southern states to the western rim of Texas, and down into Mexico. The Rockefeller Foundation was to give yellow fever the coup de grâce as far as the civilized world is concerned, but the virus is known to survive in the howler monkey living along the Amazon and in similar monkeys in West Africa. It infects workers in the jungle, but has not established epidemics in coastal cities cleared of the *Aedes aegypti* mosquito.

About the middle of November a storm hit Cuba; according to Truby, "Trees were uprooted. . . . Mosquitoes were destroyed or blown out to sea." Reed was frantic, since most of his laboratory-bred mosquitoes had died, and there were few of the dry eggs left with which to start a new batch. He persuaded his friends to go mosquito hunting with him, and they went after larvae in the water held by broken containers in a dump. Truby, writing in the 1940s, said: "A few mosquitoes were seen as can after can was pulled out of the heap. Soon we came across a galvanized can . . . that held some water. Carefully extracting it, we saw many of the beautiful, lyre-marked A.

aegypti escape. . . . Reed, Neale and Andrus secured the 'wigglers' and picked out the eggs with great glee." Andrus had another view of this outing, which he remembered years later as disgusting; the richest yield had come from cans used for toilets before the installation of a sewage system.

On November 18 Reed could write to his wife that the houses for his experiment approached completion, and that eight men were "willing and anxious to undergo any experiments that we desire to subject them to." These men were sent into the camp a week in advance of the study, and no unauthorized persons were allowed to go near it.

Emilie Reed was not enjoying the *Washington Post*'s contempt for what it called the "fumbling" of "medical amateurs" seeking information about "the causes, conditions, symptoms, and treatment of yellow fever." Major Gorgas was singled out for an attack that was off the mark, since not only was he not a central figure in the controversy at the time but he did not accept the mosquito theory. She would have been even more unhappy if she had had access to the Spanish press. *La Discussion,* a Cuban paper, ran a headline with the impact of the Spanish double exclamation points: "¡HORRIBLE IF TRUE!" In florid style, the article so headed warned:

> A rumor has reached us of a happening so horrible, so repulsive and so monstrous that resisting to believe in its existence and almost daring to deny it, we do not hesitate to publish it . . . solely as a rumor . . . in our columns. . . . Here is what is being said. . . . To those (immigrants) who remain for a short time in Triscornia is offered work in an American Camp in Quemados, promising them one dollar a day, being taken in "partys" [sic] of 30 or 40 men. . . .
>
> And here begins the horrible part. . . . At night . . . they are shut up in special habitations in which are released a large number of mosquitos which have bitten individuals suffering from yellow fever. The object of this is to study *practically* if the contagion is due or may be due to the *inoculation* from those bites. If the workman is taken sick and dies the *experiment* has demonstrated its effectiveness; if the contrary, it completely dissipates this dread.

Vindicated

The article continued to inveigh against "the most monstrous case of *humanitarian . . . savagery* which we have been witness to."

In answer to these accusations, it was immediately pointed out that one American, Lazear, had died. None of the Spaniards in the experiment died, and indeed none, American or Spanish, in the actual tests controlled or designed by Reed did die—perhaps a miracle, since twenty-three did get yellow fever. Reed went beyond the requirements proposed by the Spanish consul in having a contract drawn up in Spanish too for the consideration of any immigrant candidate. It read:

> At the completion of these experiments, within two months from this date, the undersigned will receive the sum of $100 in American gold and in case of his contracting yellow fever . . . during his residence in this camp, he will receive in addition to that sum a further sum of $100 in American gold; upon his recovery and in case of his death because of this disease, the Commission will transmit the said sum . . . to the person whom the undersigned shall designate at his convenience.

Although half a century would pass before the medical community would talk about "informed consent" and although the ethics of human experimentation was then cloudy, Reed had worked out a model consent form:

> The undersigned understands perfectly well that in the case of the development of yellow fever in him, that he endangers his life *to a certain extent* but it being entirely impossible for him to avoid the infection during his stay on this island he prefers to take the chance of contracting it intentionally in the belief that he will receive from the said Commission the greatest care and the most skillful medical service.

Kean reported that immigrants who failed to qualify as subjects because they were under twenty-four "almost wept" when denied the chance to earn so much gold so easily. And there is today a small bag of heavy material in the Walter Reed Army Institute for Research that, accord-

WALTER REED

ing to an attached note in Emilie Reed's handwriting, "held all of the gold pieces with which the men who offered themselves to be bitten by mosquitoes were paid . . . six hundred dollars in gold." This may be more myth than fact, but Kean, who was treasurer of the research fund, did recall having obtained gold coins to pay a Spanish volunteer named Antonio Benigno, who was reported to have played delightedly with them in his sickbed, asking one of his nurses to make a bag to keep his treasure in.

According to Truby:

> Each man was . . . asked if he wanted to serve. . . . All accepted. Reed did not ask any of the enlisted men to volunteer. . . . Imagine his surprise when . . . Private John E. Kissinger said he would like to volunteer. This bold step by one of the most reliable members of the detachment was a stirring and unforgettable event. . . .
>
> Reed was experiencing doubts about success with the Spaniards for difficulties had already been encountered. Kissinger's action therefore impressed him greatly and bolstered his depressed spirits. A day or two later, he was fairly beaming when he told us that John J. Moran, a civilian clerk at General Lee's headquarters, had also volunteered. Other members of the detachment . . . soon followed.

According to Hurd (superintendent of Johns Hopkins Hospital and a good friend of Reed), in referring to the same incident: "He talked with them rather fully and explained to them the dangers . . . and also added that a definite money compensation would be paid. . . . Both young men declined to receive the money and said that their only object was to further scientific investigation, whereupon Dr. Reed said, raising his hat respectfully, 'I take off my hat to you, gentlemen.' " There remain several versions of this story, but they all agree on Reed's grateful expression of appreciation.

Kissinger was bitten on November 20 by a mosquito that had fed on an extremely sick yellow fever patient on the fifth day of his attack, eleven days earlier. Nothing hap-

Vindicated

pened. When Kissinger stayed well after a second bite from the same insect on the twenty-third, it had to be concluded that the insect could not infect on the eleventh or fourteenth day after having bitten a severely ill individual on the third day of his illness. But in a letter to Truby on December 10 Reed not only thanked him for sending some mosquitoes and assured him that "the *theory* is *alright!*" but reported that Kissinger had come down with "a beautiful case" on Saturday, just 84 hours (3½ days) after being bitten on the fifth by "*two 21 day* 'birds,' *one 19 day,* one *16 day* and one *12 day* 'bird.'" The sequel was that he was discharged to go home a year after his attack and was an invalid for several years. His wife had to take in washing to make ends meet, and when their straits were reported to Congress on March 2, 1907, they were given a pension (twelve dollars a month) that was immediately rescinded. In 1910, long after Reed's death, a bill was offered to the Senate to allow the Kissingers $125 a month, but it was refused by the House Committee on Pensions, which feared to establish "a vexing precedent." It was nevertheless decided to allow the family $100 a month. Kissinger's sturdy loyalty proved expensive.

John Moran did not fall ill until Christmas Day, a victim of a bite received in the immaculate mosquito room. Members of the Reed board and two volunteers watched safely from the other side of the screened partition as the insects whined around the room and finally settled on Moran's face and hands. He observed them through a magnifying glass, and wrote an account of what he saw for the *Public Health Journal.* He must have given Reed some anxious moments, for he had made a bet with a messmate that he would be present at lunch, and he did not report his rising temperature until he had made good his wager. Thus, he was not confined in the yellow fever ward as promptly as he should have been. He was very ill indeed, recalling later that the pains suffered on Christmas night were "too intense for description—not in any particular part of my body, but in every part." His temperature was over 104°. Over the next four days the pains began to abate, he was "almost wild for want of sleep," and he subsisted on ice water, losing about twenty pounds. Nevertheless, Moran was to declare that he worshipped Reed "as a hero and will always worship his memory," calling him kindly, deeply religious, considerate, and "one of the most likeable men it is my good fortune to have known."

It was unfortunate that a man whom even Carroll described as having "a sense of delicacy" had to set up experiments on human beings, but since none of the animals that had been experimented on had contracted yellow fever, this had become an obvious if unpalatable necessity. The goal was simply to produce yellow fever in the subjects by the only way yellow fever can be transmitted, and thus to validate that way. It was hoped that good nursing would bring through all who were thus infected. Reed's fondness and concern for the volunteers, of which there is ample evidence, made him hope and pray for their survival. He suffered with each one who fell ill, and saw to it that he was nursed by men familiar with yellow fever, who would know how to cradle a patient tossed about in a seizure and who could stay calm when dealing with delirium. Kean noted that "On the earliest manifestation of an approaching infection," each man who had been bitten would be "put to bed at once and . . . carried to the yellow fever ward while occupying the same bed."

Camp Lazear had gone into operation on the day Kissinger had his first and inconsequential bite. It then consisted of seven properly floored hospital tents set up twenty feet apart. No one was allowed to enter or leave the camp from that date except three immune members of the detachment and the members of the board. Building no. 1, which was soon added to the camp, was 14 by 20 feet, with a capacity of 2,800 cubic feet. Two tiny windows facing south were heavily shuttered to keep out the sun from the dark and humid chamber in which a little stove kept the temperature above 90°. A triple door served as a barrier against mosquitoes. This kind of black hole might be expected to favor the proliferation of any foul infectious agent.

Vindicated

On the evening of November 30, Cooke and two privates, Levi Everett Falk and Warren S. Jernegan, entered it and began unpacking three large boxes of bedding and other linen stained with the vomit, blood, urine, feces, sweat, and tears of the sick being cared for in the military hospitals or lying in the morgue. After shaking the linens out, the men made up the beds, hung up the towels, and spread what was left into a bizarre festoon to allow the filth to permeate the atmosphere of their cell. Then they gingerly crept between the crusted sheets and tried to sleep. Each morning they blearily packed the linens away neatly in the boxes, and each night they unpacked them, usually adding a new shipment as they made up their beds. Their assignment never grew easier. On December 12, when a particularly nasty shipment splashed wet filth onto them as they unpacked it, they lost control and rushed into the air struggling with nausea, their surviving fastidiousness forbidding them to mingle their vomit with the black stuff that stained everything around them.

These men were of the generation newly shocked by the discovery of germs and bacteria. They knew just enough to know that there might be unseen enemies in any environment, and to have the despairing conviction that this particular environment was saturated with an agent known to be effectively malevolent. They simply awaited the first chill that would indicate the beginning of their destruction. Cooke noted that "We all felt like we were coming down with yellow fever every day." They were even more frightened when they heard about Kissinger's falling ill. If a mosquito's tiny bill could carry enough material to convey the disease, what would the masses of contaminated material around them not do? "Our squad, with one accord, developed chills of our own," wrote Cooke, "concluding that since it was so easy to produce a case of the disease in a perfectly sanitary camp, there was small chance for us to escape."

There were two reasons for hoping and praying that the men in the fomites experiment would not fall ill. Reed cared greatly about their welfare, but he also cared about

WALTER REED

proving that fomites did not convey the disease. He must have felt some anxiety also for their mental state, for the fomites experiments were enough to break down the defenses of anyone without absolute control over his physical and psychological responses to an environment that savagely assaulted every sense.

Each day the men were served the best meals the mess could provide; they ate outdoors in the sunshine. Those who managed to have any appetite for food no doubt enjoyed all that fresh fruit, newly baked bread, fresh vegetables, and Cuban coffee. They occasionally tried to play cards, but it was an effort to concentrate in the face of constant anxiety. Their time was up on December 19. None showed any signs of the fever, but they were kept in quarantine nearby for five days in case they harbored some latent infection. Some credit should go also to these patients who had been denied the comfort of a change of clothing and bed linen in order to supply uniquely nasty material for the experiment; in late December two subjects slept in the "very garments worn by yellow fever patients throughout their entire attacks" and never washed.

Throughout this trying period Reed kept up his usual voluminous correspondence with his wife. It is interesting that although their style contained much precious but no doubt affectionate chaff that sounds patronizing today, his letters did convey a great deal of sober information about his work. He commiserated over "the Gout in her darling foot and 'toseys,'—but he also told about enrolling volunteers and reported that the Spaniards in camp had told Agramonte "that they had never had so much to eat or been treated so kindly in all their lives and that they expected to get yellow fever anyway, when they went to Havana." He explained to her that if it took twelve days in August to arm the mosquitoes with death-dealing material, it might take eighteen to twenty-four when the thermometer dropped at night to 61°, as it had been doing at the time he wrote, huddled in an overcoat "with doors and windows all closed and lamp burning full tilt." Since none of Emilie's correspondence remains, we cannot know how much she grasped of his work except as it affected the status and comfort of her family, but it would be unfair to conclude that the more sober passages in his letters to her went unappreciated. She must for many reasons have rejoiced in a letter sent on December 9, after Falk and Jernigan had obliged by contracting the fever from a bite as planned (although Jernigan had to have four bites). It read:

> Rejoice with me, sweetheart, as aside from the antitoxin of Diphtheria and Koch's discovery of the tubercle bacillus, it will be regarded as the most important piece of work, scientifically, during the 19th Century. I do not Exaggerate, and I could shout for very joy that Heaven has permitted me to establish this wonderful way of propagating Yellow fever. It was Finlay's theory and he deserves much for having suggested it, but as he did nothing to prove it, it was rejected by all, including Genl. Sternberg. Now we have put it beyond Cavil. It's [sic] importance to Cuba and the United States cannot be estimated. Major Kean says that the discovery is worth more than the cost of the Spanish War including lives lost and money expended.

A few days later he wrote again: "Hurrah! I will write to Dr. Sternberg in a few days. . . . Of course, he will, at once, write an article and say that for 20 years he has considered the mosquito as the most probable cause of yellow fever. That would be just in order for him to do so." His surmise was correct.

One of his letters reported a visit paid to one of his patients by several doctors, Gorgas and Albertini among them. Albertini had declared at once that the disorder was clearly yellow fever, but the others adopted a wait-and-see attitude. Reed ascribed such equivocation to reluctance to admit the defeat of their various theories inapplicable to the case in hand. Wasdin, for example, fairly wailed in the press over the way in which acceptance of Reed's claims would negate "all the years of disinfection" with which his branch had been so self-righteously busy.

It was no doubt with a special satisfaction that Reed sent cablegrams to his chief keeping him abreast of such findings as "Four cases within period of incubation; diagnosis confirmed . . . by Guiteras and others. Inoculation successful in eighty per cent." He noted that one patient whose case was mild had taken sick such a short time before the quarantine period ended that he "could have passed quarantine on the morning of his sixth day, and would have been the focus of one of those epidemics ascribed to infected bedding, or the unpacking of a trunk." He then told Sternberg of the next step he proposed —dividing building no. 2 by a partition of fine screening, and stationing control subjects in one half while loosing infected mosquitoes in the other. The purpose of this was to determine if, by any chance, there could be any infection carried on the air.

There was still more to learn, and Reed addressed himself to a number of questions: Could the larvae of an infected mosquito retain the poison when they became adult mosquitoes? Could an injection of blood from a person with the fever convey it to another? Just how small could the parasite (still invisible) be? It was to be nearly a year after the Reed board established that subcutaneous injection of whole blood could convey yellow fever from one person to another that Carroll carried out experiments with the ultra filtrate of whole blood that Reed had planned. At this time, while Reed was in Washington, he began to have serious doubts about infecting any more volunteers, even to get additional valuable information.

CHAPTER XI

A Holiday Season
and a Let Down

Emilie Reed did not want to spend the forthcoming
Christmas season without her husband. He had
scotched her plan to have him return to the States: "Of
course, I am just as anxious to come as can be, and I am
looking forward with perfect delight to the time when I
can come, but it won't be before Christmas," he wrote.
Then she proposed that she join him in Cuba. "Concerning your coming," he replied, "nothing would delight me
more . . . *if* I only had some place for you to get your
meals. You couldn't mess with us, as things are."

Jessie Carroll had also objected to being alone over the
holidays, and her husband wrote that

> Dr. Reed . . . is very much elated, because we have ob-
> tained a true case of yellow fever from the bite of his
> experimental mosquito and this confirms our former re-
> sults. The idea is to read another paper before the Pan-

WALTER REED

American Congress . . . February 5, so it will be necessary to wait here until then. He acknowledges the great importance of our work and said, it should entitle us to membership in any of the European Medical Societies. In addition, the U.S. Gov't. should award a sum of money for the work, but that is all speculation . . . some benefit must certainly follow.

This should be our consolation for spending a lonely Xmas and a year hence I hope our position will be much better than now.

Reed's letters to his wife just before Christmas ranged from asking her to give Blossom a gift from him to gloating about having "infected two men by injecting the blood of a case under the skin of the healthy individual" and thus proving that the parasite is in the general circulation and can be conveyed by a needle as well as by a mosquito's bite. And in one of them he voiced for the first time a breathtaking dream; the long distance runner cannot fail to give some thought to applauding crowds at the finish line." Calling her "Miss Gouty" in reference to her painful foot, he wrote, "You will change your mind [about disgust with his absence over the holidays] when you are 'Mrs. Surgeon General' . . . holding big receptions on K St.!"

Although it was at Christmas that some of the experimental subjects underwent their harshest experiences, Christmas in a Latin country is a time of great festivity, and there were parties everywhere. Reed felt that he could now go to at least a few to which he had been invited. The first was one arranged at the request of General Wood at the Havana Delmonico's to honor Carlos Finlay. Everybody came to what Reed reported as "a very recherché affair"—all those who had for years turned impatiently away from the old gaffer with the obsession about mosquitoes, listening impatiently when cornered by him but surreptitiously glancing at their watches and shrugging that Latin shrug, smiling and shaking their heads as soon as he left. Now, as nearly as the Americans could tell, they

A Holiday Season and a Let Down

were competing with one another in eulogizing Finlay in impassioned Cuban Spanish, with Agramonte in the lead. It was hard to keep up with the staccato Spanish, but it was fun, with all the waving of hands, the dramatic lowering of the voice, and histrionic pauses. Agramonte's rhetoric could be heard over the popping of champagne corks as he deplored the "many years we fumbled in the darkness of our own ignorance for a means of control against this awful malady" and "the inefficient and costly disinfection." He regretted the "fruitless search for a specific remedy and the means of immunization" that had been such "a fruitful source of reknown [sic] and revenue to well known scientific humbugs." He had known all along, he said, that the "persistent and inconsistent Sanarelli" and his corps of "experts" would fail, for their work was "not instigated . . . by that holy sentiment of humanity . . . not by the natural thirst for knowledge and the truth which urges the truly scientific man"—but "by a bastard feeling of commercialism, a hope for early and abundant lucre, regardless of the means or of the consequences."

The climax of the evening was the presentation of a bronze statuette to Finlay. Destined to live until 1915, after many accomplishments and many awards, Finlay must have thought that night that he was attending his own wake, so fervent were the eulogies. Reed was pleased to hear Guiteras, the master of ceremonies, give full credit to the Reed board for its discoveries even as he congratulated Finlay on his concepts. And General Wood went on record as holding "the confirmation of Dr. Finlay's doctrine the greatest step forward made by the medical sciences since Jenner's discovery of the vaccination." Everyone had a good time. Even Kean, whose Spanish was primitive, seems to have felt more at home among the ebullient Cubans than he had among Bostonians who spoke the mother tongue, however astringently.

Carroll was not made merry by the season, but sulked instead. He stayed away from the reception because he "had no evening dress and no blue uniform to wear" and was "ashamed to go and be the only person present in Khaki which is intended only for a field uniform." He recalled with chagrin having gone to another gathering attended by "the best physicians of the city," at which everyone wore evening dress and his uniform made him "very conspicuous." He felt left out, writing that "The officers of the German Man of War Veneta were invited out to the post yesterday to a luncheon," which was followed by a review of the troops. "I was not invited to the luncheon and only saw the review," he told Jessie, and although he had been asked to the reception on the Veneta, "as it was rather a swell affair and a number of ladies were to be there I did not go." Worst of all, he confided, was that Reed would not only not do anything to advance him, but had spoken harshly to him "right in front of the General and that was not something that a man would forget." Besides, the fever had broken him; he continued to suffer from neuralgia and a boil on his neck. Reed himself had a severe toothache, and there was no dentist to take care of it.

Two Army wives, Mrs. Stark and Mrs. Kean, managed a home-style Christmas celebration for their friends and the children on the post. They trimmed a guava bush for a Christmas tree, and had gifts for everyone. The children's gifts were suitable toys, but the grown-ups' were pointed and chosen for fun. An especially bibulous officer was given a miniature water wagon. The very slim Stark got a cake of "obesity soap" guaranteed to wash away unwanted pounds. Reed was given a small object that had been hard to wrap and had wiry appendages sticking out in all directions. He laughed heartily at it, but paused in the middle of the hilarity to think of the implications of this homemade mosquito, and of Moran, tossing in pain in the yellow fever ward. There was a verse attached to it.

> Over the plains of Cuba
> Roams the mosquito wild
> No one can catch or tame her
> For she is Nature's child.

A Holiday Season and a Let Down

With Yellow Jack she fills herself,
And none her pleasure Mar,
Till Major Reed does Capture her,
And puts her in a jar. . . .

This "brought down the house" according to Reed, who confided to Emilie that since the punch was "very enjoyable, the occasion was anything but dull."

Reed no doubt missed the cold, fir-smelling crackle of a stateside Christmas season, but he did enjoy the gaiety —writing home that "I feel as if I hadn't had any sleep for a month. Wednesday night the entire garrison assembled at Cap't. Waterman's for a progressive euchre party, where we laughed, played and ate good things till about midnight." He was sorry Emilie could not have seen "the style and dress of the Cuban ladies at the Governor General's Ball," which a thousand people attended. "Music for Dancing was furnished by a military Band stationed in the Park outside," he wrote. "The night was just like summer. . . ."

In spite of all the festivity, he was beginning work on a presentation for the Pan-American Congress to be held in Havana. He was pleased that Sternberg had made him an official delegate. As he looked back on the eventful year just past, he spoke several times in letters to his wife of his gratitude for the fulfillment of his "daily prayer that I might live to do some good for humanity," adding he hoped that a cure for yellow fever would be "wrought out in the early days of the new Century." And after outlining in a letter to Sternberg newly developed refinements in his study that should be included in the Pan-American report, he asked that his group be relieved from duty in Cuba and authorized to "return to our proper station" immediately after the close of the congress. He planned to continue in his laboratory in Washington his search for the parasite, using material gathered in Cuba. He asked also that the buildings at the camp at Quemados be left standing so observations there could be resumed "when the epidemic year begins again."

Even before the Pan American Congress convened, Kean and Wood began a campaign against mosquitoes in Cuba on the basis of the Reed board's early findings. Gorgas, Havana's chief health officer, was reluctant at first, since although he was "convinced that the mosquito *could* convey yellow fever," he was not yet "prepared to believe that it was the only way or *even the ordinary way* of conveying the disease." He allowed, however, that inasmuch as mosquitoes were implicated at all, it would be well to take measures against them.

After his euphoric period, Reed had to face not only Gorgas's lukewarm approval but smouldering hostility in his erstwhile assistant, Carroll. That Reed was not the only target of Carroll's disaffection can be seen in the devastating surliness of something he wrote to his wife: "Don't trouble to send me any more letters that do not contain anything of interest to me." Even as Reed was writing to the surgeon general trying to get him advanced in rank, Carroll wrote to her:

> I send you today's Havana paper in which I have marked an editorial paragraph referring to our work in which great credit is given to Drs. Reed and Agramonte and I am not mentioned. A newspaper man was out . . . and R. gave him an interview. That and the way Gen. Wood's name is mentioned tells where the information came from. It was inspired, of course, by R. . . . I think I shall forward the paper to Gen. S. direct so that he may see how the thing is going.

Then he decided not to send it, saying that he would "wait until after the Army Bill passes and see if I get a chance as a Vol. Major. Nothing better will ever come to me."

Dr. Alvah Pinto, who had commanded the hospital during Carroll's stay there as a patient, was also disgruntled. This was not clearly apparent at the time, but if the animus he exhibited when interviewed forty years later is any indication, his presence could not have been felt as supportive and cordial. He chose to remember Reed's work day in Cuba as one of less than continuous personal toil and described him as having been "a very austere man, very much impressed with his own knowledge," one brooking no disagreement. There is a grudging ambivalence in Pinto's assessment: "He was smart and knew about everything, but he was a man to whom you had to prove what you said. . . . he was domineering . . . a good friend, but he insisted upon you being worthy of his friendship." Quite possibly Pinto's attitude arose from the fact that he was never honored for having been a volunteer, since, although not known to be immune, he had not contracted yellow fever after being bitten experimentally by infected mosquitoes.

Even Leland Howard, that helpful Washington entomologist, inadvertently did his bit to detract from Reed's accomplishment. In a book he published in 1901, he indicated that Reed had been sent to Cuba with specific instructions from Sternberg to work on the mosquito hypothesis. When this error was pointed out to him, he attributed it to the fact that he and Sternberg had talked at such length about the possibilities of yellow fever transmittal at their many meetings at Washington's Cosmos Club that he had made an unwarranted assumption about Reed's orders.

Kean was busy with practical applications of what the board had learned, "Experimenting all day with petroleum oils of various densities to test their different ability on water and their power to kill mosquito larvae." Howard had sent along suggestions about the most efficient way of using kerosene on water in which mosquitoes bred. He was also useful in straightening out a confusion of mosquito types that Reed wanted clarified before delivering his paper.

Lest Reed become smug with success, fate had a truly low blow in store for him. On January 17, 1901, he was charged by the army for being absent without leave. Although the charge grew out of a bureaucratic mixup chiefly focused on his attendance at the Indianapolis meeting in October, and on the fact that when service on an examining board had conflicted with his real work, his superior officer had given him verbal orders to skip the examining board, the charge was serious. On May 14, 1901, just before he was volleyed back to Cuba, the army demanded an explanation of his absence from an Army Medical Examining Board for which Sternberg had —unfortunately, by phone—appointed substitutes. Reed replied that "As this is the first time, during a service of nearly 26 years, that I have been called upon for an explanation of absence from or neglect of duty of any description whatever, this communication becomes to me the source of very great personal and professional humiliation." Happily, Sternberg rose to the occasion and vindicated him, but it had been made abundantly clear that the leash the army kept him on was short, and could be reeled in at the will of any faceless official.

It is no wonder that the authorities had a hard time keeping up with him, for his Cuba-to-Washington shuttle had been rapid. But the charge had done little to make easier the preparation of the paper for the Congress. And if he had thought that his message would startle American medicine once he had delivered his paper, he was mistaken. The reporter assigned to cover the congress for the *Journal of the American Medical Association* had looked forward to his visit to Cuba, but he was dismayed to find that Spanish was spoken everywhere, even in the congress, and that accordingly the general sessions held nothing for him. He claimed that many of those whose names appeared on the program never appeared, and that this was particularly true of those expected from the States. The reporter perked up when General Wood took the floor, noticing with some satisfaction that "The house was filled with the elite of the city, in all the glory of full dress and Spanish beauty," and when one Eusebios Hernandez gave the principal address in Spanish, the reporter was not unhappy although the subject of obstetrics he thought certainly not very appropriate for a mixed audience. Small wonder that Reed's presentation was given no more than a carelessly written paragraph!

Although the reporter indicated that anyone interested

A Holiday Season and a Let Down

could turn to the paper as it was published in the *Journal,* it was not published as submitted, although the gist was there. Reed had listed himself as the author along with Carroll and Agramonte and had given their work the title "The Etiology of Yellow Fever, An Additional Note." He began by reviewing the earlier presentation he had made before the American Public Health Association, and went on in painstaking detail about how Kissinger and the three Spaniards had been given yellow fever by mosquitoes and about how Cooke and the six volunteers who had lived in the building full of fomites had *not* contracted it. He concluded that the mosquito known then as *C. fasciatus* was in truth the intermediate host of yellow fever, and that it did transmit the infection to the nonimmune "by means of the bite."

He explained that it took about twelve days after contamination before the insect could convey the infection, and that its bite before that much time had elapsed did not confer immunity. He spoke also of direct transfer, saying that "Yellow fever can also be experimentally produced by the subcutaneous injection of blood taken from the general circulation during the first and second days of this disease." He emphasized that one attack confers immunity and noted a wide variation in the incubation period —from forty-one hours to five days and seventeen hours.

Then he made a statement that had considerable economic meaning—that yellow fever is not conveyed by fomites, that disinfection of any object supposedly contaminated by contact with those sick with yellow fever is unnecessary. He pointed out that "A house may be said to be infected . . . only when there are present within the walls contaminated mosquitoes capable of conveying the parasite of this disease." The implications of this were, of course, important to trade.

He said further that "The spread of yellow fever can be most effectually controlled by measures directed to the destruction of mosquitoes and the protection of the sick against the bites of these insects." He acknowledged that the agent remained mysterious, that "While that mode of propagation of yellow fever has now been definitely determined, the specific cause of this disease remains to be discovered." By then he suspected that Sternberg might have been right in holding that the agent of the disease was too small to be identified by any technology available. Nine years earlier, Sternberg had talked of "the possibility . . . that the specific infectious agent . . . may belong to an entirely different class of micro-organisms from the bacteria, or that it may be ultra-microscopic, not capable of demonstration in the tissues by the staining methods usually employed by bacteriologists."

Although Reed's paper was well received, there were those in the audience who could hardly wait to disagree or disapprove. Dr. Luis Perna from Cienfuegos did not find the mosquito vector hypothesis new or interesting, and he was shocked at the way yellow fever had been investigated in "experiments on human beings" and wanted his disgust at such experiments recorded. Dr. San Martin, on the other hand, strongly defended what had been done, and Dr. H. B. Horlbeck of Charleston, South Carolina, rejoiced that "the problem of 200 years was about to be solved" and that now old quarantine measures could be modified, if not abandoned. Dr. Emilio Martinez of Havana defended human experimentation when necessary. Dr. Manuel Gutierrez of Mexico accepted the results of Reed's experimentation as "incontrovertible," although they reversed all that he had hitherto believed. Juan Guiteras claimed that Reed could summon yellow fever at will, like a wizard, but since several physicians thought that he might have the wrong mosquito, the discussion veered off into entomology.

Finlay disagreed with some of the conclusions. According to *JAMA*, he believed that "the differences between his opinion and that held by the Commission" would disappear, noting that his conclusions had been based on the study of three varieties of mosquitoes, whereas the commission had studied but one, and asking that the commission reconsider its "hard and biased rules." Whatever

A Holiday Season and a Let Down

Finlay truly meant by what he is quoted as having said, Reed simply thanked the audience for its attention, and added: "In regard to the moral aspect of the case, he did not think that any one appreciated the position in which he found himself," and, noting that the first experiment had been made on Carroll, a member of the board itself, he indicated where that pale survivor of the pestilence sat in the audience. Carroll was thereupon given a real ovation. Apparently, the audience was considerably more spirited and the subject considered more interesting than the *JAMA* reporter appreciated. Reed felt the enthusiasm, as he was to write to Emilie: "I received dozens of the warmest kind of handshakes from Cuban, Spanish, Mexican, South American, and North American physicians, men whom I had not even met. The hall was crowded and even the doors packed with listeners. It was indeed a signal triumph of our work."

It was fortunate that he had this moment of warmth, for the *Washington Post,* which had not sent a reporter but which appeared in quarters influential in the making or breaking of reputations, published an article that showed small respect for his achievement.

> They [the authorities in Cuba] now solemnly announce that "the specific cause of the disease is unknown." They also state that it is "not due to dirt"—something the yellow fever specialists of the South have insisted on for the past sixty years. But they do say that the disease, the origin of which they cannot specify, is transmitted only by mosquitoes. There has been some affectionate wrangling on this point, one side contending that all mosquitoes can communicate the poison, while others maintain with great valor and determination that only the gray-legged variety is gifted. . . . But all are agreed that the mosquito does the business and we must branch out from that.
>
> . . . We should like to offer the suggestion that since the controversy has been finally settled the yellow fever board and the Pan-American Medicals generally can well afford to cease their experiments upon inoffensive persons . . . if these gifted scientists are now convinced that the mosquito

is the real and only medium of infection, why not devote themselves to the eradication of the medium instead of killing more people by way of academic demonstration?

Carroll wrote to Jennie that he had teased Reed about this article, and before long let her in on a secret; he was confident in his illusion that he had found the parasite —that hitherto unseen element the mosquito transported. She was to tell no one.

By then Reed was back in Washington, so busy grappling with infuriating details of publicity and bureaucratic intransigence that he might have begun thinking of his days in Cuba as a pleasant tropical interlude. He was enraged at the liberties taken by *JAMA* in the publication of his congress paper and was fully aware that Sternberg was blandly taking more and more credit for the work on yellow fever. He hated having to notify Carroll that he "need not look for any promotion" since "the secretary refused to fill any vacancies caused by Major Kean's or other vacancies under that particular act," being able to hold out hope only that Carroll might be sent to the Philippines, where Reed thought it would be folly for him to go.

His need for money had put him quickly back in harness teaching night classes at the Columbian, he was serving on an examining board, and the last thing he needed then was to have the government refuse him some medical records he wanted for further confirmation of the period of extrinsic incubation. But a clerk in the Record and Pension Office had been so militarily briefed about yielding medical records that when Reed put in his request he was treated like a beggar off the streets—an offensive one, at that—and when General Ainsworth was appealed to, he only grudgingly permitted Reed to make some notes from the record, and required him to make those on the premises.

Small wonder that like many other men with similar frustrations, he began to think about a chicken farm—one his sister Laura proposed establishing, the prospect of which led him to say ruefully, "The only thing that I ever

A Holiday Season and a Let Down

knew anything about is raising chickens!" The letter in which this was discussed seems to have been written after a long gap in their correspondence, for in it he told the story of all that had been going on in Cuba. He took the occasion to preen himself a bit before the sister he had always helped, though seldom as much as he wanted to.

> After much work and thinking, I am glad to say that we have been able to prove conclusively that yellow fever is propagated only by the bite of a certain kind of mosquito, provided it has bitten a case of yellow fever about 12 days before. My friends pronounce it a very great discovery and some even write to me that, for America, it means more than any discovery for the last 100 years! Dr. Carter, of the Marine Hospital Service, writes that my discovery makes me one of the greatest benefactors that the human race has ever had! Of course, when one has left wife and baby, faced death and won a victory, it makes him happy, but it shouldn't turn his head. He should only thank God that his life hasn't been in vain, and go on about his business.

By now much of what Reed still fondly thought of as his business was in other hands. Guiteras, a convert to the mosquito theory, was continuing work toward the development of an immunizing agent. With colleagues he was organizing a vaccination station at the Las Animas Hospital with the support and approval of General Wood and the counsel of Gorgas, Finlay, Albertini, and the hospital's director, Ross. Having some serious misapprehensions about the disease, Guiteras felt that a severe attack could be expected from the bite of an insect that showed "excessive virulence," although how this characteristic could be assessed is a mystery.

Guiteras tried to develop a suitable experimental colony of mosquitoes by having a patient "introduce his hand through a straining bag . . . adjusted permanently to the mouth of [a] jar, and . . . let it rest inside . . . until the . . . insects would get filled." After the hand was withdrawn with care that no insect escape, there was a wait of from twelve to seventeen days—"the time needed for the insect to acquire pathogenic properties."

WALTER REED

It is said that on one occasion when Gorgas was showing a group from the International Sanitary Congress how his work was conducted at Las Animas, he introduced them to an exhibit that included mosquito eggs, larvae, and pupae. Then he showed them some mosquitoes just hatched, and pointed to mature insects "ready to convey yellow fever," as he said. As he showed these to the dignitaries, many of whom had expressed skepticism about mosquito transmittal, the mosquito netting accidentally slipped and let the mosquitoes soar about the room. According to Gorgas, the men "stood for a moment dumfounded. . . . Then each one of the twenty, at the same time made a rush for the door . . . the pressure from behind toppled it over onto the ground four feet below, and in a moment, there were some twenty gentlemen in a pile on the ground struggling to get as far as possible" from what they thought were deadly insects, although they had not yet fed on a patient but were only in readiness to do so. "Our visitors laughingly acknowledged that, at any rate, their unconscious selves had been convinced of the correctness of the theory of mosquito transmission."

Not until well into July were Guiteras and Gorgas able to get infected mosquitoes and go ahead with their work, which turned out to be ill-fated, with the loss of three out of eight volunteers. A plucky twenty-five year old nurse named Clara Maass, who volunteered in order to nurse yellow fever patients better, was bitten by laden mosquitoes four times without harm, but her fifth inoculation was fatal, and her death evoked a public demand that all such experiments be terminated.

A year before, a directive had gone out from the headquarters of the Department of Cuba in April, written by Kean, stamped by General Wood, and now defining disinfection as "the employment of measures aimed at the destruction of . . . mosquitoes" fed on yellow fever patients. It suggested fumigation, either with sulphur, formaldehyde, or insect powder. It specified, probably to the great relief of people who remembered the burning of houses and quarantine enforced at the point of a gun, that

A Holiday Season and a Let Down

"So far as yellow fever is concerned, infection of a room or building simply means that it contains infected mosquitoes." But Kean had been so diligent in doing what was needed that by May the Havanese were no doubt tired of the scent of smoking pyrethrum. Each household had its own cistern or rainbarrel, which had to be filmed with oil to destroy the wigglers. Puddles had to be drained, as well as old cans, bottles, tins, and anywhere that water could harbor the larvae. It was a herculean task, but by the end of May the number of deaths from the fever in Havana could be counted on the fingers of one hand. Gorgas's interest at that time was in carrying out his orders; he remained skeptical that fumigating against mosquitoes was the whole answer, clinging to the belief that something still lurked in fomites. And Reed, back in Washington, feared that overly zealous fumigation would lead the Cubans to conceal any mild cases that might erupt, perpetuating the foci for a spread of the disease. By mid-June, however, Havana was almost free of it, for the first time in 150 years. No one could believe it.

Reed wrote to Kean about this time, acknowledging that the identification of the responsible parasite remained a mystery. He had just talked at length with the surgeon general about the Englishman Durham. It turned out that he had never cultivated it after all. Reed noted that he did not share Kean's hope of finding some immunizing method. "*Protection* & Prevention," he wrote, "are far, far more important. The *fundamental facts have been established,* the others are of secondary importance."

In writing congratulations to Gorgas on the turn of events in Havana, he could not resist warning him lest "the head of our Corps . . . claim all the credit for it." He went on, "You might tell Dr. Finlay, too, with my best compliments, that he had better look to his laurels as the proposer of the Mosquito Theory, since Dr. Sternberg, in an article in the July Pop. Science Monthly, puts forward his name . . . for the credit for our work in Cuba." He warned, "Dr. Finlay's turn will come," and referred to his chief as "The ungodly—." He was in a fury: "He knows as well as I do, that he only mentioned Finlay's theory to *condemn* it!"

Things continued to go well in Havana, and by July 20 Gorgas was able to tell Reed that there was still no yellow fever there. Reed replied at once, generously insisting that this was due to Gorgas's work and diplomatic handling of the situation: "A man of less discretion, enthusiasm and energy would have made a fiasco of it—whereas you, my dear Gorgas, availing yourself of the results of the work at Camp Lazear, have rid that pest hole Havana, of her yellow plague. . . . Thank God that the *Medical Dept.* of the U.S. Army, which got such a black eye during the Spanish-American War, has during the past year accomplished work that will always remain to its eternal credit."

He anxiously inquired whether Gorgas had omitted all disinfection of bedding and clothing, hoping earnestly that this was the case, for in his forthcoming presentation before the American Public Health Association he was counting on pointing to the work accomplished in Havana *without* the disinfection of such material.

He must have been gratified in April, when he spoke before the University of Maryland faculty in Baltimore on "Recent Researches in Yellow Fever," that his old friend and teacher, Dean Welch, spoke of his work as being next in importance to the discovery of anesthesia. But his audience at a meeting of the Medical Society of the District of Columbia in May wanted to back him into a corner and get him to define the mysterious invisible cause of the disease. They did not realize that no one at that time, with the technology then available, could possibly isolate and see the agent. It may become visible today with the use of an electron microscope—a roomful of exquisitely precise equipment; but it is alive in ways still being debated. DNA and RNA were half a century in the future. Current belief classifies a virus as a bit of RNA or DNA that may be said to be alive because it can use some other cell's chemical system to reproduce itself a hundredfold before ruining the cell itself.

Although Durham did come to Washington, he had

A Holiday Season and a Let Down

originally asked to join the Reed board in Cuba "for the purpose of trying to reconcile his work, or rather the results of his work, at Para, Brazil, with our observations at Quemados," but Reed had not seen why he should return "just to enable Dr. Durham to try to reconcile things that I must, at present, consider irreconcilable." He preferred, he said, to spend the summer in the States. But it was not proximity to the office of the surgeon general that was the attraction in Washington, for not only did Sternberg seek on every possible occasion to claim the yellow fever victory for himself, but the vexing question of who would succeed him was making things very uncomfortable—giving rise, as such situations are apt to do, to the sharpening of old resentments and the eruption of new ones. One fellow army surgeon thought to be under consideration was named Pope. O'Reilly, a devout Catholic, was a strong candidate, and this explains Reed's comment in a letter to Kean, who had just become head of Charities and Corrections for a Cuba beset by poverty and starvation, that "the Pope has the Dead Cinch on the Chair of Moses" (referring to Sternberg). Reed felt that some Catholic conspiracy was going to triumph, and at least O'Reilly did become surgeon general before long.

CHAPTER XII

"Prize me no prizes, for my prize is death"

On September 6, 1901, William McKinley, the president of the United States, was shot by an assassin in Buffalo, New York, during the week the American Public Health Association was meeting in that city. Walter Reed was about to present his paper on "The Prevention of Yellow Fever" when the event took place, and several of his friends and at least one of his enemies were among the consultants who hovered over the fallen president until he died on September 14.

What might have been a gratifying reunion with an old professor was less than happy. Dr. A. N. Bell, who had taught Reed years earlier at the Brooklyn City Hospital, was unable to yield any of his pride in his crusades to have imported rags sterilized (and hence his belief that fomites conveyed many ills, including yellow fever), and attacked his former pupil for failing to acknowledge this route of transmittal. Eugene Wasdin, Reed's old opponent, took issue vociferously with him again, maintaining that although yellow fever apparently *could* be transmitted by mosquitoes, that was not the only way, and that when it was conveyed by a mosquito it was "but an artificial infection such as we produce in animals in our laboratories, and as Dr. Reed has produced in man with his hypodermic syringe independent of the stegomyia." (This name for *A. aegypti* persisted for some time.)

It must have been hard for Reed to keep his composure while he stood aside at the podium after making his presentation, and heard Wasdin:

> . . . appeal, as an officer of the Marine Hospital Service who has served at the National Quarantine Stations, and has honestly done his duty in investigating this disease . . . to this Association against the proposition to modify our quarantine restrictions, since it is not reasonable to accept the unproved dictum that yellow fever is transmitted solely by the stegomyia fasciata, if by doing so we displace the theory that has given us safety all these years.

One is hard put to understand what Wasdin meant by *safety,* since there had never been any safety from yellow fever. Although Reed gave a lengthy, sound, and reasonable rebuttal, he allowed himself one histrionic flourish: "You should not forget that yellow fever is such a peculiar disease, that while a patient can infect his clothing in New Orleans, he cannot do so at Asheville, N.C. or at Atlanta, Ga., even though he die with black vomit!" It may have been that Wasdin was by then already exhibiting signs of the mental disease that, tragically, would necessitate his subsequent confinement in a mental institution and his death there.

This experience might have kept Reed from entertaining any high hopes about becoming the new surgeon general, but the possibility was being discussed at embarrassing length among his friends, of whom Kean was the most energetic. Kean was not only devoted to his friend, but he seems to have realized that prizes do not necessarily go to the deserving. His search for support in no way detracted from his gentlemanly sense of honor, but simply showed a grasp of reality perhaps a bit more worldly than Reed's. After thanking Kean for his support, Reed demurred: "But, Commandante mio, when you and others ask me to enter into a bitter struggle for the Surgeon Generalcy, you ask me to do what my better sense tells me to avoid." He admitted that he would be less than candid if he denied any such ambition, and confided "only to . . . one of my best friends" that he thought that the work he had done in Cuba, with its commercial implications as well as its relief of suffering, did deserve some reward. But that did not mean, he went on, that he should "enter the struggle with Brown, Smart, DeWitt, O'Reilly, Pope, Hoff, et al." since "to do so, would be utterly repulsive to my feelings, for I am so old fashioned as to believe that the office should seek the man and not the man be compelled to beg for the office." He further explained that he could not take his case to General Wood, as Kean suggested, for the very reason that Wood had been so complimentary about the Cuban accomplishments. "If it came from him unsolicited, then I, like any other man, would feel very much flattered, but I would rather die a thousand deaths than to be put in the attitude of a beggar!"

Kean was not so easily swept aside, however, and in mid-October he reported that on an inspection trip with Wood he had seized "a chance to have a heart-to-heart talk . . . and lost no time broaching the subject which I had at heart—the 'vitalization' of the Med. Corps by the appointment of a certain Distinguished Scientist to be S.G." Wood, he said, had "in his quick straight-forward way" agreed to do everything in his power to have Reed appointed, saying that he would talk to the president in November in the belief that Reed deserved the post "far more than any other candidate." Wood had already given the president his opinion that the Reed board's findings were "worth the entire cost of the Spanish war," and he confided in Kean his regret that Reed had been worried about Sternberg's aggressive claims to the credit. "He further said that he was going to mention the matter . . . in a way that would make it perfectly clear that the S.G. had nothing in the world to do with it." "What more do you wish?" crowed Kean. "I think O'Reilly's Hanna pull isn't in it with the lead-pipe cinch that you have on things."

Cautioning his friend in Washington to "follow the tactics of Bre'er Rabbit and keep on saying nothing for the present," Kean advised against arousing any "unnecessary antagonisms either of Uncle George Miller [Sternberg] or the Marine Hospital Service." Soon Reed wrote to Cuba that "The plot . . . thickens. Several new candidates for ye Uncle George Miller's boots have appeared on the horizon." In view of the entry into the race of a number of junior officers, Reed asked why Kean did not enter himself. Brushing aside this suggestion, the loyal Kean offered some political analysis: Wood and Roosevelt were both "strenuous fellows," and energetic men were unlikely to think the worse of another who went vigorously after a prize to which he was entitled. His aristocratic confidence is clear in his remarks to Reed that "the constant breathing of the balmy ether of scientific life has made you a little—will you excuse the word if I say finical in your attitude toward this matter." He noted that in spite of the motto *Palmam qui meruit ferat,* it was up to one who truly deserved the prize to "stand before the judges and put out his hand for the palm."

In the same letter he ruminated about what Carroll could expect in his continued search for the critical organism. "What sort . . . can pass through a Pasteur filter? It must be almost molecular in its smallness, and far beyond the reach of the microscope. . . . A serum-therapy may now perhaps be easy to find, but if you waste your winter teaching . . . some other fellow may get on to it."

By the end of November there was a throng of contenders for the surgeon generalcy. In mid-January of 1902, Kean was confident on the basis of conversations with General Wood that his friend had a good chance for it. Wood quoted Elihu Root, the secretary of war, as having spoken of the need for administrative ability in the post, and the need to avoid getting "another George M." Throughout the unusually cold spring of 1902, Reed's candidacy—although endorsed by Osler, Welch, and the presidents of Harvard and the University of Michigan, among other supporters—continued to hang fire. As late as May, Reed wrote to Emilie, who was with Blossom in the mountains, that he had had a visit with Kean, and that after a mint julep the two friends had decided to campaign actively. "We are out for blood—*B L O O D!*" he wrote.

On June 7, however, the *Army and Navy Journal* announced that Col. William H. Forwood would succeed Sternberg on June 8 to serve until his forthcoming retirement, after which a choice would be made from a list of candidates among whom Reed was not mentioned at all. Such an abrupt termination of a dream, however marginally believed in, is bound to leave a certain emptiness in anyone.

In June, Reed was invited by General Wood's adjutant general to attend a dinner being given in Boston to honor Wood and three members of his staff. He was surprised but frankly pleased to be given the second place of honor himself. And immediately thereafter he received two honorary degrees, an L.L.D. from the University of Michigan, honoring "Walter Reed, most eminent physician, famous for his investigations of the causes of diseases"; and an M.A. from Harvard, whose citation, written in Latin, honored "The army surgeon, medical graduate of Virginia, who planned and directed in Cuba the experiments which have given man control over that fearful scourge, yellow fever." Such attentions must have done something to heal the hurt from being virtually overlooked by his own medical corps in its choice of leader.

Meanwhile, Reed continued to be in touch with Gorgas in Cuba. Early that year, while the surgeon generalcy was still undecided and he was accordingly perhaps a little overdefensive, he had taken the occasion to tax Gorgas with what he called , half playfully, "an awful perversion of facts." In a published interview with Gorgas, credit for

the proof of yellow fever transmittal was assigned—or so
it seemed—to "Finlay and the American." Reed told his
old friend that "I know that you didn't intend to say it, but
somehow I suppose that being back in Havana you feel it
your duty to 'honey up' that simpering old nabob
[Finlay]. . . ." Gorgas's reply was prompt and to the point.

> I do not plead guilty to any such statement as you quote.
> You and our chief must have been on a tear the night
> before you got his conversation mixed up with the objec-
> tionable article. I do not "honey fuggle the simpering old
> idiot" a bit. I think he is an old Trump as modest as he is
> kindly and true. His reasoning for selecting the Stegomyia
> as the bearer of yellow fever is the best piece of logical
> reasoning that can be found in medicine anywhere. I
> acknowledge that the less . . . said about his experiments
> . . . the better for the old Doctor's reputation as a scientist.
> . . . You are the great man in the matter. His theory would
> have remained an idle dream except for your work and all
> that the sanitary department of Havana has accomplished
> . . . is due to your demonstration. . . . Your name will be
> remembered in medicine with Jenner and Wills [sic] long
> after the old Doctor has been forgotten so do not begrudge
> the old man his little meed of praise.

Gorgas was himself entertaining a dream at the time—the
dream of being the chief medical officer on the "Isthmian"
canal. He was, of course, sent to Panama as he had hoped,
and during World War I it was he who presided over the
medical corps as its surgeon general. The next letter from
Gorgas reached Reed, according to his own account, "in
the midst of an exciting faculty meeting called for the
purpose of deciding whether at our coming school
commencement . . . the Faculty & Student officers should
march in columns of fours . . . or should proceed in
double file!" His irritation over having to bother with
anything so picayune no doubt gave extra emphasis to his
statement that they would both have *"to go on that TOOT,
when you land on your native heath, once more!"*

In August, changes at the Columbian University Medical School made Reed chairman of general pathology, and

Carroll, who had returned from Cuba by then, an associate professor of pathology and bacteriology; Reed's stipend for the year was $500, Carroll's $275. In September, Kean arrived in Washington as head of the division of supplies, and the families of the two old friends occupied apartments in the same house, one owned by Dr. Kober. Kean's work was inadequately staffed at first, and the confusion that awaited him—as well as Sternberg's behavior toward Reed—led him to analyze what he saw as the deficiencies of Sternberg's time in office. He decided that Sternberg was a very able scientist who had taken office with little administrative experience and no particular acumen in judging men, and that he had accepted the organizational patterns he found. When their inefficiency became evident, he simply worked harder himself instead of demanding appropriate help, and he became so enslaved by the details of his office that lists of the supplies for a hospital ship written out in his own hand remain in the record. This was not, Kean realized, the kind of chief who would be warm and ready with congratulations for one of his men, or able to see the symbolic value of celebrating a task well done.

In a letter to Gorgas that Reed wrote two months before his death, he noted the appearance of still another article in the *North American Review* in which their chief again claimed credit for the work done in Cuba. What is of greater interest, however, is his reference to a matter that the new surgeon general had, to Reed's embarrassment, referred to him for decision. This was apparently a request from Gorgas to be allowed to go on with experimentation on human subjects. "Of course," he wrote Gorgas, "I had to advise against further experimentation on human beings along the lines suggested by you. Not only my own experience, but also Guiteras' . . . has given me a horror of any further human experiments." He anticipated that Gorgas would be angry, and asked that they wait until his anger had a chance to cool, after which, since Gorgas was coming to Washington to join the faculty of the Army Medical School, the writer hoped his friend would "be willing to forget all over one of 'Hancock's Best.'" Gorgas and Guiteras went on a sad wild-goose chase, hoping to verify one of Finlay's mistaken notions: that a mosquito that has bitten a person with a mild case of yellow fever can then transfer a mild case. This belief was held despite such obvious evidence as the difference in what had happened when the same mosquito bit both Carroll and another person.

Reed's stature seemed to be recognized chiefly in ways that placed greater burdens on his shoulders. In November, when the librarian of the Surgeon General's Library died, Reed was given that post in addition to his other obligations. He had always wanted it. He held it for only twenty-three days, during which time he had been ordered by the army to investigate the epidemic of typhoid fever that had broken out among troops at Fort H. G. Wright on Fisher's Island, New York. He told friends he was so exhausted that he could not remember having written some of the lectures he delivered that fall. And when Louis Flexner asked him to speak at the University of Pennsylvania, he declined, saying that he had hardly thought of yellow fever for a year, but had been engaged since returning from Cuba in "nothing but hum-drum every day military duties . . . which from their very monotony have almost reduced me to a condition of hopeless idiocy."

A change in him was beginning to be evident to those who were close. His wife thought each day took a year's toll, and was concerned when he himself spoke of being so weak in mind and body that he found lecturing a problem. He kept up his good spirits when in company, but it became known later that he once told his faithful old messenger at the museum that he considered himself "a very sick man."

He was in pain on November 12, and after coming home from the office he was unable to go out again for his lecture. Claiming that he must have eaten something that disagreed with him, he took to his bed until nearly noon on the thirteenth, when he made an unsuccessful attempt

"Prize me no prizes"

at resuming his schedule. He thought of appendicitis, but his medical friends were not so sure. Later on Friday, his friend William Borden thought him sick enough to be sent home in Borden's carriage, and they agreed that since his abdomen was sensitive to the touch in the significant area, it would be well to operate by midweek. But by Sunday he felt well enough to want his usual Sunday-morning waffles, which his wife sternly denied him. She was to recall that "he sat up in bed most of the day, read his papers, talked of the improvements we were to make in our summer home in the Spring, what we would plant in the garden and so on." Although visitors came in the afternoon, and were welcomed by a man who did not seem unduly upset, by night—when his temperature rose significantly —Borden and Kean decided to operate. His wife left a rather puzzling but pathetic account of their last night together: "I was not brave enough to speak and if he was in pain he gave no evidence of it."

He refused a stretcher the next morning when he went to the army hospital at Washington Barracks. He even stopped on his way out of the house to write a check. Before going to the operating room, he told Kean, "I am not afraid of the knife but if anything should happen I am leaving my wife and daughter so little." And his last words before the ether took effect were "so little, so little."

The surgeons were dismayed at what they found. Borden later said that his patient's symptoms had "in no way indicated the gravity of the . . . trouble." At the side of their unconscious patient stood the ranking members of the Army Medical Corps; Forwood, O'Reilly, Kean, and others are known to have been there. They agreed that his poor reaction was no doubt a result of his poor general condition at the time. Peritonitis developed, although this was not evident for three days. But the symptoms exhibited on the fourth day showed the breakdown of the tissue that they had hoped would keep the potentially infective material within the gut. By the time Kean assessed the situation on November 22, he knew that death was but a few hours away. Walter Reed died on November 23, 1902, having just missed being made a colonel at fifty-one. There was no autopsy, but the swollen appendix, saved in a bottle, was dutifully stored in the Army Medical Museum, where it remained until it was thrown out in the late twenties, perhaps because of the parsimony of the Depression years. My opinion is that he had an amoebic infection of the cecum, maybe from all of the infected fruits and vegetables he ate in Cuba. In any case, common bacterial appendicitis and peritonitis were usually fatal then, and may even be fatal today.

Walter Reed was buried from St. Thomas's Church in Washington on a dark and rainy day. Officers of the medical corps were the pallbearers; there was a large crowd of mourners. When the Episcopal service was over, his flower-covered casket was taken on a caisson to Arlington National Cemetery. The funeral cortege was met on the Virginia side of the Potomac by several troops of cavalry from Fort Myer, and at the interment a volley of three shots was fired by way of farewell.

His wife was not there. She had not gone to the church, to pray along with the others for "the soul of the faithful departed." However many conventions we establish for getting through the unbearable, one cannot judge what is in the heart of another at such a time; there was talk of her being under the care of a doctor. Emilie Reed had not visited her husband in the hospital according to Kean —who took charge of the family and brought Blossom to what was almost the deathbed scene at the army hospital in Washington Barracks. When, several decades after Reed's death, his widow wrote a partially historic, partially fantasy, account of their life, she mentioned two visits, but these seem almost certainly a result of the vagaries of memory rather than an account of fact. She also wrote: "He had often told me that he did not like deathbed scenes and *he* was spared that agony. . . . I have been willing to add the crushing sorrow of that week's separation to my heavy burden feeling that in some slight way I *spared* him." She may very well simply have been incapacitated by terror,

"Prize me no prizes"

not only of death itself but of what the future held for her with no one to provide for her or to sustain her.

Before a year had passed, a meeting to establish the Walter Reed Memorial Association was held in Bar Harbor, Maine (on August 15, 1903). Notices of this meeting had appeared in medical journals, and invitations had been sent to certain people in the medical world and to other leaders. Present was a company of great men that would have gladdened Reed's heart, although it might have puzzled him. The contingent that represented his Johns Hopkins experience included President Daniel Gilman; William Henry Welch, his special teacher; Dr. G. Janeway; Alexander A. Abbott, an associate during Reed's study there; Lewellys F. Barker, now temporarily at the Rush Medical School in Chicago; and Dr. Christian Herter from Columbia. From outside the medical community came philanthropists John Stewart Kennedy and Morris Jessup, and Bishop William Lawrence of Massachusetts, Emilie's distant kinsman. The goal of the organization was to raise a fund of $25,000 or more, from which the income was to provide for Emilie Reed and her daughter and which would eventually finance the erection of a suitable monument in Washington to Reed's memory. Its incorporators included Alexander Graham Bell; George Miller Sternberg; Robert M. O'Reilly, recently become the new surgeon general; James Carroll (lamentably still a first lieutenant); the same Dr. A. F. A. King with whom Reed had had such lively exchanges; and Drs. G. Wythe Cook and Charles W. Needham. Sternberg was president of the association in his day, and so were Gorgas and Kean somewhat later.

It was not easy to raise even $25,000 at a time when a major in the army made only $1875 a year, but the response was heartwarming, if not financially overwhelming. Fortunately, the contributions from the members of the medical corps was augmented by token benefactions from Rockefeller and Morgan philanthropy, but there were other handsome individual gifts, including one from

President Charles Eliot of Harvard and one from Bishop Lawrence. General Wood, Gorgas, Sternberg, and Finlay were contributors. The desired sum was realized, although it took four more years to raise it.

Emilie Reed lived to be ninety-six, receiving much-needed help from the fund until she died in 1950. Blossom died in 1964, and it was not until this obligation to Reed's family was at an end that the association could erect its proposed memorial. Meanwhile, an act of Congress in 1905 authorized the construction of a general hospital for the army, and this was named for Walter Reed. Maj. William Borden, the close friend who had operated upon Reed, was a steady worker on behalf of the proposed medical center and was most influential in getting the important people to support it. The Walter Reed Army Medical Center was created in 1923, fourteen years after the opening of that general hospital. This center includes the Walter Reed Army Institute of Research, the corps' historical unit, and several other specialty units. The association was able, in collaboration with the Cuban government, to have Camp Lazear preserved as a memorial to that promising young doctor who lost his life in yellow fever research and to his colleagues. The association's memorial, a marble base supporting Reed's bust, was dedicated as recently as November 21, 1966, and commands a beautifully landscaped spot in the Walter Reed Medical Center.

Ever since the establishment of the Walter Reed Army Hospital, Reed's name comes to public attention whenever an ailing statesman or military commander is brought there. One suspects that although Walter Reed might feel perplexed, and surely awed, he would be at home with the patients and solicitous of their welfare. It is a pity that to some his name has become simply a label applied to an imposing governmental institution; one might hope that it would evoke more often the winsome presence of a steadfast and vital but always sensitive man who truly killed a dragon.

Epilogue

I n retrospect it becomes clear that I have tried to bring Walter
Reed to life not simply as "a medical hero" but as a man as
well. I have found strength in his belief, early received and never
rejected, that something was expected of him, rather than that
society owed him much.

His story can remind us as we sit in the cunningly decorated
offices of "planners" that until only recently man worked with raw
materials, seldom in comfort and often at risk. It helps one's
perspective to recall—when seated in the comfort of an airport
lounge waiting to cross the country in a few pampered hours—the
young couple lurching along, day after day, in an overladen and
appallingly rigid wagon, upheld as much by their modest delight
in learning to know one another as by the unfolding surprises of
the far-stretching Indian country.

Although contemporary man owes much to Walter Reed for his
part in freeing us from a particularly agonizing disease, another
aspect of his legacy may be even more important—the model of
what it is to be a good and faithful servant.

WALTER REED

What makes an ordinary man a great one? From a simple and loving home, Walter Reed was secure in his principles and his faith supported him, though in perfect modesty, in a special form of bravery, the intellectual courage of his convictions. His plain but sturdy training was not unusual. Other men saw what he saw and knew what he knew and shared his compassion. The flash of insight at the right time makes the difference. There we step into the magic of a life.

Index

INDEX

Index

2° Div. Hospital 7
Camp Columbia.
April
Maj. Ira C. Bro